THE EARLIER
INHABITANTS OF
LONDON

THE EARLIER INHABITANTS OF LONDON

BY

F. G. PARSONS, F.R.C.S., F.S.A.

"Also the citye of London, that is to me so dere
and swete, in which I was forthgrowen; and more
kindly love have I to that place than to any other
in yerth, as every kindly creture hath full appetite
to that place of his kindly engendrure, and to wilne
reste and pece in that stede to abide."

Chaucer "Testament of Love";
book I., sect. 5.

KENNIKAT PRESS
Port Washington, N. Y./London

THE EARLIER INHABITANTS OF LONDON

First published in 1927
Reissued in 1971 by Kennikat Press
Library of Congress Catalog Card No: 78-118492
ISBN 0-8046-1240-4

Manufactured by Taylor Publishing Company   Dallas, Texas

CONTENTS

LIST OF ILLUSTRATIONS

FOREWORD

THE historian of to-day understands quite well that the question of race is one which he has to consider, and for which he has to make allowances, as he searches and weighs the records of the past.

He knows that events almost the same may have results quite different when they happen to groups of people of different physical and mental characteristics, and he is beginning to ask the anthropologist to take his share in the team work, upon which all modern research is becoming more and more dependent.

This book is a contribution, however small, of facts collected during thirty years' work at the physical anthropology of the inhabitants of these islands ; and especially of London.

Some of it is quite technical, and here the reader is asked to take a good deal on trust. Much, however, is so straightforward that all educated men and women may grasp it ; and, when once the lines of enquiry are understood, this part may be added to, and checked, by anyone who cares to bring to the task industry, and the wish to be accurate.

It is well that the historian should understand clearly how little, as well as how much help he may expect from Anthropology in its present state. Before he expresses disappointment that more information is not forthcoming from the daily increasing stores of material, he should realise that bones cannot be read like coins; for each one is the result of a living process, and has been moulded into its shape by the action of muscles, ligaments and other soft parts. A particular mark on a coin may, in the hands of a numismatist, date it absolutely; but a particular mark on a bone may only show that its owner used some special muscle rather strongly. Then, too, all the peculiarities due to age, sex and disease have to be recognised and allowed for. The need for this, of course, limits the ranks of physical anthropologists to those who have had a full training in Anatomy and Pathology, and are fortunate enough to be able to find time for the interesting, though unremunerative, study of Anthropology.

The question of race, which underlies all the following pages, has been woven into the history of Early Londoners, partly because the writer is a

Londoner, and has always been interested in the records and antiquities of the City, and partly because its early history is attracting many investigators and writers nowadays to whom it may be a help to see the point of view of the anthropologist, even though they may feel obliged to disagree with some or all of his conclusions.

Finally the author would like to say how much he owes to Mr. Fallaize and to Dr. Mulligan for greatly needed advice, and for help with the proofs.

St. Thomas's Hospital,
    S.E.1.
1927.

THE EARLIER INHABITANTS
OF LONDON

CHAPTER I.

PALÆOLITHIC AND NEOLITHIC MAN

IT is not always possible, nor is it always desirable, to be strictly logical ; hence, in writing of the earlier inhabitants of London, I do not feel that I am limited to the time when the place was actually called by that name ; even if I knew definitely when that time began.

It is commonly said that the name is derived from the two British words *Llyn*, a lake, and *Dynas*, a fort or dwelling place ; and it seems apt enough when we think of the twin gravel mounds, rising above the London clay and capped with brick earth, which now are known as Ludgate Hill˙ and Cornhill. In hills of this formation water is easily obtainable from shallow wells, and nowhere in the neighbourhood could a better site for a settlement be found.

The first part of the name, Llyn, suggests that, when it was given, these hills were more or less surrounded by tidal marshes and lagoons ; but the derivation of place names is proverbially difficult to trace. Some of the modern students of linguistics believe that the name may go back to an older tongue than the Celtic ; and hold that, in any case, Llyn is a modern Welsh word, not used by the Britons in Roman or pre-Roman days. If this opinion gains general support among those who study the ancient British language, it will be a serious blow to the hitherto accepted derivation of London's name. But this is not all ; for Gordon Home, in his interesting book on " Roman London," has gathered geological evidence to show that about two thousand years ago, only a little before Cæsar's time, the banks of the Thames were two feet higher instead of lower than they are now, and that, therefore, the idea that London was surrounded by marshy pools must be seriously reconsidered.

Undoubtedly he is right in thinking that the land all over the south of Britain was once higher than it is now ; and the fact that trunks of oak and yew trees are found in the marshes below Woolwich and Erith, shows that these marshes were once forest. Many geologists and botanists, however, agree that the period of land elevation passed away about 1800 B.C., when Britain became an island ; and, in any case, it seems certain that there were marshes round London in A.D. 43, for Aulus Plautius, we are told, owed to their treachery the loss of many of his men. Modern research, then, only allows us to say that London is a name which is mentioned first in A.D. 61, after Boudicca sacked it, and that probably it is a Roman adaptation of a Celtic or pre-Celtic name, though of its meaning we have at present no sure knowledge.

The earliest human evidence which we have about London's site is that during the year 1926 part of a female skull was found in the excavations for Lloyd's Bank in Cornhill, and at such a depth that it probably is one of the earliest human remains in Britain, rivalling even the famous Piltdown skull in age. After this woman roamed over the spot where Cornhill later on was to be formed, the land must have sunk beneath the Thames, which then became so broad that it stretched from the Hampstead to the Sydenham hills. From this wide river, gravel and brick earth or river drift were deposited over the hinder part of the skull, and since this was all that was found of the skeleton, it is possible that the rest may have been washed away.

Later on, after how many thousand years we can only guess, the land began to rise once more, and at one period, between 3000 and 1800 B.C.,* is said to have been sixty feet higher than it now is. After this geologically very short upheaval, there was another equally rapid settlement, leaving us, when history begins, with a marsh bordered river, most likely wider and shallower than it is at present.

*Q. Journ. Meteorological Society, July 1921.

Bones of the rhinoceros, hyæna and hippopotamus, on the one hand, and of the mammoth, on the other, are found in London excavations. The former tell us that at one time the climate was subtropical; the latter, that, later on, it became bitterly cold. No doubt these and many other animals were hunted or fought by the men of the old stone age, for their chipped flint implements, dating back as far as the Chellean period, possibly two hundred thousand years ago, are found. Good examples of these may be seen in our London museums.

The skulls of these palæolithic people varied a great deal, and our conception of them is being modified year by year as fresh material comes to light. Many of them are of a low type, such as the Piltdown and the Cornhill skulls appear to have been, and show many likenesses to those of the anthropoid apes. It must be realized, however, that the old stone age was a very long one, and modern discoveries are opening our eyes to the fact that many of these people had skulls as large and almost as well formed as our own. Probably the later people of the old stone age were very like those of the new, and the improvement in the make of their stone implements does not coincide with any marked change in their anatomical characters. Grasping this probability, many anthropologists use the term Neanthropic to cover the later stages of the palæolithic and the earlier stages of the neolithic age, and do not allow that the difference in the implements used forms a sharp boundary line, as was formerly believed.

That there has been a continuous occupation of London since the days of the old stone age is clearly impossible, because since then the whole site has been at the bottom of the Thames, and the modern contours of gravel and river drift have been deposited. Indeed, if the present geological estimate is right, viz. that our twin hills rose for the first time from the river bed about 3000 B.C., they must have been welcomed by people well advanced in the neolithic culture; and would have found the country largely occupied by the Mediterranean Race, about which I shall have much to say hereafter.

In spite of this, however, it is quite probable that some of the blood of palæolithic man still lingers in our veins; and there are anthropologists of great experience who hold that the characteristics of these people may still be traced in the heads and features of men walking about the streets of London to-day.

There is every reason to believe, then, that the earliest neolithic men were the direct descendants of the palæolithic; and, like them, were hunters and fishers. Their numbers could only have been small because game, when it is too much hunted, soon leaves a district, and when it wandered away they would have been obliged to follow it. There was nothing to stop them from passing to and from the Continent, since Britain was part of it, and probably few of them slept for two nights running in the same spot. Some of them, however, seem to have made caves their fixed home ; and lately the Spelaeological Society of Bristol University has been working scientifically through the limestone caves in the Mendips, and has added much to our knowledge of these people.

Some of them, called by Huxley the " River Bed Race," seem to have lived in rough shelters by the banks of rivers, where they caught fish, either by spearing them or with hooks and lines. Others, in a more advanced stage, may have brought from the Continent the art of pile driving, and made lake dwellings on piles, though we cannot point to any satisfactory proof of their presence ; for the Glastonbury pile dwellings belong to a later period ; while the river bed people who lived at Sunbury, and used deer horn picks, may have been pile dwellers, but have left no certain evidence of it. But though the neolithic folk certainly were often in the neighbourhood of London, as their polished flints in our museums bear witness, there is nothing to show that they ever made a permanent settlement there ; indeed, if the number of flints gives any clue, they were more numerous up the river at Twickenham or Kew.

As time rolled on they learned to domesticate animals, thus ensuring a steady supply of meat and milk, which must have allowed their numbers to increase very much ; but the most epoch making discovery, since that of kindling fire, was that the seeds of certain grasses might be ground into flour, and that by cultivation these plants could be made to yield much more plentifully. Of course it is not hinted that any of these discoveries were made in Britain. It is much more likely that they were brought here by wanderers and adopted very slowly ; but, once adopted, the people were changed from wandering hunters into a settled agricultural community.

As to what they were like, there seems to have been little difference between the earlier neolithic inhabitants of Britain and the Mediterranean Race, which I shall now have to describe. The same long narrow heads and low orbits were common ; and the skulls of a series of the River Bed Race, which I measured and recorded many years ago, were as high and as capacious as the average of the 14th and 15th century inhabitants of Rothwell in Northants, whose skulls lie in the crypt below the Church ; and who, I think, may be taken as representative mediæval Englishmen.

It is an old standing belief among anthropologists that a fairly pure branch of one of the three great races or stocks, which, by their blending in various proportions, have formed nearly all the nations of Europe, migrated slowly westward along both shores of the Mediterranean ; always keeping near the sea, and occupying the various peninsulas of Southern Europe—Greece, Italy and Spain—in its long trek, which must have taken many thou-

sands of years in its wanderings.   When Spain was
occupied, these people turned North, and worked
up through France to Britain, which probably at
that time was not separated from the Continent,
as it is now.   The numerous sandbanks in the
Channel recall this subsidence, and suggest for
what a length of time the passage from the Continent to Britain need have given no trouble to newcomers.

The name of the Mediterranean Race has been
given, happily enough, to these wanderers, and,
since they buried their dead, or at least their
illustrious dead, under long mounds or barrows,
they often are spoken of as the Long Barrow Race.
In speaking, as so often I shall have to do, of the
three primitive races of Europe—the Mediterranean, the Alpine and the Nordic—a word of
caution is needed.   The conception of the three
races is a very valuable one, and helps us to clear
thinking ; but it is only a working hypothesis,
since we never have found any of these races
absolutely pure.   Still it is certain that in the
South of Europe the main type of mankind is
that of a small, dark, longheaded people which we
call the Mediterranean Race ; in the North of
Europe that of a tall, fair, long-headed type called
the Nordic Race ; while in the centre, especially in
the neighbourhood of the Alps, is a thickset, short-
headed people, known as the Alpine Race.   Most
anthropologists see no reason to believe that
a change of locality modifies these characteristics

to any marked extent ; but hold that, when races interbreed, some of the characters are dominant or more powerfully handed down than others which are called recessive. Most modern Europeans, therefore, if their anatomical characters are examined carefully, show a mosaic pattern, and no doubt the same is true for their mental traits. It is very seldom that we meet with a man of pure Nordic or Mediterranean type ; but in a group of men from any one place there usually is no difficulty in deciding as to which race shows up most clearly in the patchwork.

Whence originally the Mediterranean people came we do not know, but they can be traced to the eastern part of the Mediterranean ; and some of the earlier Egyptians (Proto-Egyptian) resemble them wonderfully in the general characters of their skulls.*

It now seems that this route through Spain and France was not the only one followed by people from the East of the Mediterranean to the West of Europe and Britain, for evidences lately have been found that some of them took a short cut through the Danube and Rhine valleys, leaving behind them peculiar, gourd-shaped pottery which is spoken of as a relic of the Vinča culture. Unfortunately we have as yet no knowledge of the physical characters of these people, but the fact that their pottery imitates gourds suggests that they came from some place, such as Egypt or

*Elliot Smith, *Ancient Egyptians*, p 41.

Asia Minor, where gourds were common and could be used as vessels. It may be that they were a branch of the Mediterranean Race taking a different path of escape from an overpeopled neighbourhood, and there are reasons to think that some of their culture was that of Troy.

Probably the Mediterranean Race was the people referred to by the older writers in Heroic times as the Pelasgians, who formed the background of low born folk so easily routed and put to flight by the bronze clad Achæan, Nordic heroes.

It is difficult, however, to discuss Eastern Mediterranean anthropology without opening up the question of Minoan culture, which would lead us too far afield.

Besides their habit of raising long barrows, these people had another; that of erecting menhirs, or upright stones, and dolmens, or stone tables, examples of which are quite common in this country as well as all along the route which they followed in their migration. These were almost certainly associated with their religion, which probably included rites for human sacrifice ; and, likely enough, were handed on to their descendants in part, the Ancient Britons. Indeed it is held by some that Druidism was a survival of the religious cult of these Long Barrow Folk, and that when we hang up a branch of mistletoe at Christmas, we are keeping alive a rite which has been handed down from father to son for many thousands of years. Also many think that Stonehenge, or at least part of it, was the work of these people rather than, as formerly was held, that of the Round Barrow or Beaker Folk ; but patient work is going on at that monument, and when it is finished we shall very likely know more.

If we bear in mind that these people, when they came, were in the pastoral stage, it will be easy to understand the attraction which the open chalk downs of Wiltshire and Dorsetshire, as well as the moors of Yorkshire, had for them ; and when the size of the great upright stones of the monument at Stonehenge and the weight of the cross stones set upon them are realized, there can be little doubt that large numbers of men, spurred on by a common religious impulse to set up something which should last for ever, must have dwelt within easy reach of one another.

I have wandered, I fear, a long way from London ; but it is impossible to study the earlier or, indeed, the more modern Londoner, without making every effort to understand this striking race which formed a part in the mixture of which he is composed.

Although the chalk downs of Wiltshire suited them and their flocks so well, Kent seems to have appealed to them too ; for on the road between Maidstone and Rochester stands the well-known trilithon called Kit's Coty House, the foundations of which have, so far as I know, never been systematically explored. It is usually said that this monument formed the core of a barrow, the earth of which has been removed by neighbouring farmers ; but, though this may well be true, it must be remembered that other barrows have not been so treated, and certainly in Henry the Eighth's time it was as it is now, for Lambarde describes it.

Just opposite it, on the other side of the Medway, at Trotterscliffe, stands a similar monument known as the Coldrum Rocks, under which some long skulls, seemingly neolithic, were found. From their position these two monuments have been regarded as beacons which showed the place at which the neolithic trackway, later known as the Pilgrims Way, crossed the river. Not far from Trotterscliffe, in Addington Park, are hundreds of megaliths, many of which have fallen, though some still stand. Here also, it seems that a large number of these stone raisers must have lived and worked while their sheep pastured on the neighbouring North Downs.

Truly it appears that one of the most striking characteristics in the mentality of the Long Barrow Race was the desire to raise, no matter at what cost of labour, monuments which would endure throughout all time. For this reason one is inclined to ascribe to them those little understood artificial mounds, found in various parts of the country, such as Silbury Hill, the mound at Marlborough College and, perhaps, the Dane John at Canterbury and Primrose Hill. Excavations have hitherto shown nothing embedded in these ;

and one is left hesitating as to whether they had only a religious significance, or whether they served some useful purpose in the shape of landmarks, observation posts, or signalling stations ; but, whatever their purpose, it is clear that they were made by a people of imagination, able to conceive things on a large scale and to carry out their conceptions by patient, well-organized team work and no little mechanical skill. Such people undoubtedly were the Long Barrow Folk.

If I have succeeded in arousing any interest in these people the reader will want to know what they were like, physically and mentally ; and, in trying to find out, we must be careful to separate what we know from what we may reasonably infer. On the physical side are the skeletons found in the long barrows, for the preservation of which we owe a great deal to the memory of Thurnham, Davis and Rolleston. Of course, in dealing with these, we must think carefully whether the barrows are likely to contain only the bones of the race which made them or whether those of slaves or enemies of some other race are included ; for it has lately been pointed out that much of the craniological work done in the Pacific is misleading ; since the skulls found in any one island are so often those of enemies from another.

In the case of the long barrows there does not seem to be much fear of a mistake of this kind, because although, as has been shown, the country was almost certainly inhabited by neolithic hunters and fishers when the Long Barrow People began to arrive, these must have been so few that, even if a mixture of the races did take place, the effect on the long barrow type of skeleton would have been inappreciable.

The skeletons found in the long barrows are those of small, slightly built people, the males averaging about 5ft.4in. and the females little over 5ft. in height, as deduced from the length of their thigh bones. Like most other primitive races, their thigh bones were flattened in the upper part of the shaft, a condition known as platymeria ; while the shin bones were often flattened too, but from side to side, and not from before backward, as were the thigh bones. This latter condition is known as platycnemia ; and the two are associated so often that a common cause is suggested. I am convinced that neither of these characteristics has any racial significance, but that both are the result of the action of certain muscles in the squatting position, and might be brought about in our own young people by depriving them of chairs and stools.

In studying the skulls it is important not to generalize on one or two chance specimens, and still more important not to do so on one or two picked specimens, but to collect as many as possible, and then to separate the sexes as far as may be. This last qualification is necessary because it is doubtful whether any craniologist, however great his experience, can determine unerringly the sex of more than seven or eight skulls out of ten ; but since the doubtful two or three have failed to tell their sex to his trained eye, they are not likely to affect the average to any great extent.

In the accompanying figures* are the contours of male skulls of the Long Barrow Race, selected by me from the collections at Oxford, Cambridge and London because they were perfect enough to be drawn. Since the contours were made, I have had it pointed out to me that the Cissbury skull was probably not Long Barrow at all, but belonged to an earlier race ; possibly the early neolithic about which we have been speaking. This mistake, which, having been made, should be acknowledged as widely as possible, has not, I think, affected the results to any great extent, since the characteristics of this skull are common to most of the others.

The object of the investigation was to produce a set of average contours of male Long Barrow skulls which might be contrasted or superimposed on others obtained from different races. Tracings were made with a dioptograph, a machine which ensures that each skull is drawn from exactly the same point of view, and that the foreshortening effects of photography are done away with. The tracings having been made, a very large number of measurements are taken from each,

*From a paper on " The Long Barrow Race and its relationship to the Modern Inhabitants of London."—*Journ. Anthrop. Inst.* Vol. 51. p. 55.

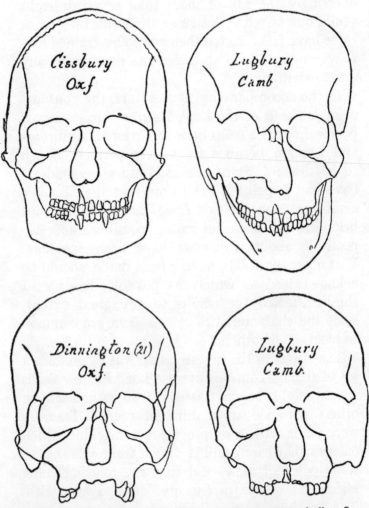

FIG. 1. Dioptographic tracings of Long Barrow skulls. In each case the upper name records the site of the barrow, and the lower, the museum in which the skull may be found.

(The Cissbury skull probably belongs to a branch of the Neolithic Race, which was earlier than that of the Long Barrows.)

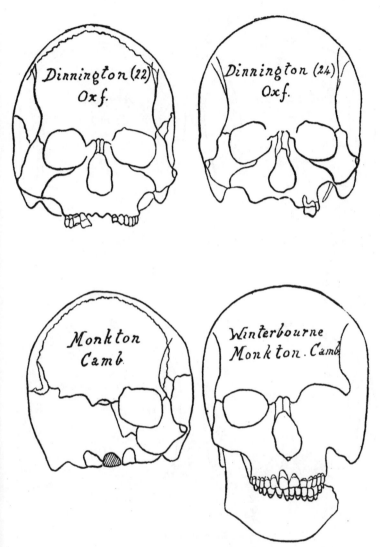

FIG. 2. Face views of Long Barrow skulls.

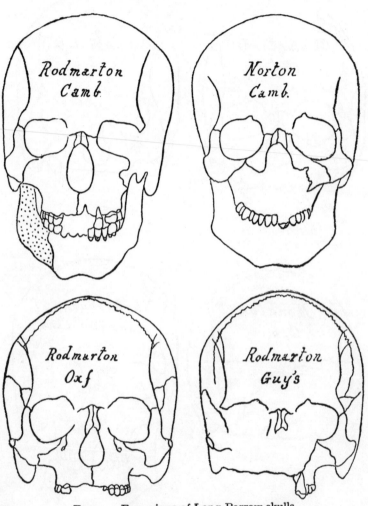

FIG. 3.   Face views of Long Barrow skulls.

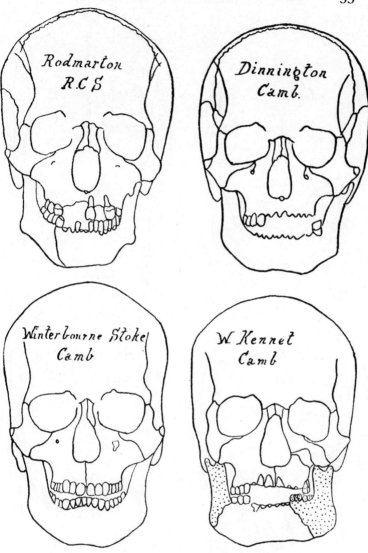

Fig. 4. Face views of Long Barrow skulls.

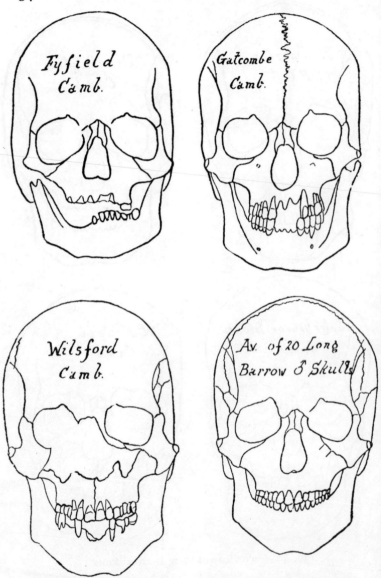

FIG 5. Long Barrow skulls. The lower figure, on the right-hand side is a composite tracing of 20 skulls. Its height, above a line joining the lower margins of the orbits, shows that the average is 117 mm., while its greatest breadth gives an average of 140 mm,

some of which it is possible to check with the calipers from the actual skull. When this is done the averages of all the measurements are worked out and a new drawing made, which should be, and really is, an average of the series. It is impossible here to give more than a mere outline of the method which, of course, abounds in technical detail and can be learned only by practice. Two criticisms of this piece of work have reached me and are important. The first is that the author has been biassed insensibly by his preconceived ideals of what a Long Barrow skull should be like, and has picked only those which approached

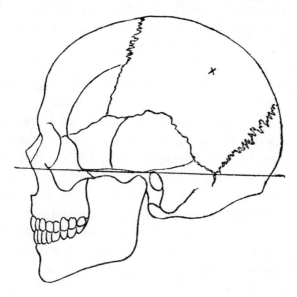

Fig. 6. A composite tracing of the profiles of 20 male Long Barrow skulls, the average length of which is 196 mm. and the height above the top of the ear passage 117 mm.

his standard ; while the second suggests that the skulls had such a large range of variation that little value could be placed on averages obtained from so small a number.

It is satisfactory to think that each of these criticisms cancels the other. The first, of course, is difficult to disprove except by quoting the second, or by saying once more that all the available measurable skulls were taken ; but the second may be tested by working out the co-efficients of variation in several of the measurements, taken at random. This has been done, and the result proves that the series is really a homogeneous one, since the co-efficients are lower than those obtained from large series the homogeneity of which has never been questioned.

After studying the crania from various points of view, it is clear that we are dealing with a race the average length of whose skulls is 196 mm. This, of course, means little until we have something with which to compare it ; and in order to provide this I will insert here a table, taken from "Man," which gives the lengths and breadths of various groups of skulls and living heads recorded in the British Isles up to the present time. It is necessary to lay stress upon the fact that all these records were taken from adult males only, and that further information may be found in the original paper.*

*Man, Vol. XXII, February 1922, p. 19.

TABLE OF CRANIAL MEASUREMENTS

	No. of Records.	Length.	Breadth.	Index.	
ANCIENT					
Long Barrow Folk	20	196	140	71.4	Measured by Prof. W. Wright.
Beaker Folk	36	180	150	83.3	
Celtic British (N.E. Yorks)	23	186	136	73.1	
Anglo-Saxons (6th and 7th Centuries)	44	190	143.5	75.5	
MEDIÆVAL					
Saxon Canons	8	190	142	74.7	
Rothwell Crypt	100	186	142	76.3	Rothwell, near Kettering Northants
Dover Crypt	12	185	143	77.3	St. Peter's Church (demolished).
Upchurch Crypt	16	184	144	78.3	Near Rainham, N. Kent.
Hythe Crypt	322	179	143	79.9	St. Leonard's Ch., Hythe, Kent.
MODERN					
Whitechapel	135	189	140.7	74.4	A 17th Century Plague Pit
Moorfields	42	189.1	143	75.6	Do Do
Claremarket } (Macdonell)	30	188	142	75.5	18th centy. burial ground
British soldiers	42	187	141	75.4	19th centy. soldiers (R.A.M. College, Mill-
East England	30	184	143	77.7	Chiefly agriculturists (bank.
Somerset	101	184	141	76.6	Do Do
Bristol Hosp. Patients (Beddoe)	80	186	143	76.9	19th centy.
London Patients	150	185	142	76.8	From St. Thomas's Hospl.
N. Chilterns	200	187	143.5	76.7	Dr. Bradbrooke
N.E. Kent	52	186	144	77.4	Dr. Witney
British soldiers	124	183	141	77.0	During Great War (1916)
British criminals	3000	183.7	142.4	77.5	
Educated British	182	189	145.6	77.0	Mostly living in London
Medical Students	233	186	145	77.9	From St. Thomas's Hosp.

From this table it is plain that a cranial length of 196mm. is distinctly long even in a long headed community like the British.   In the same way it it will be seen that the average breadth of 140mm. is quite a low one.   But, since the anthropologist wishes to convey some idea of the shape, as well as of the actual size of the skull, he quotes the breadth in percentages of the length, arriving at his result by this simple formula

$$\frac{\text{Breadth.} \times 100}{\text{Length}} = \text{Cranial Index}$$

Tested in this way, the cranial index of the skulls under discussion is found to be 71.4, that is to say their breadth is 71.4 per cent. of their length ; and when the list is referred to, it will be seen how low an index this is.   A word of warning for those to whom the subject is new may save misunderstanding : it is that the Cranial Index is not the same thing as the Cephalic Index, where the measurements are recorded of the living head, though one index may be converted into the other by adding or subtracting 8mm. to or from the length and breadth, to allow for the thickness of the soft parts.   The index will not do more than it professes, and it must clearly be understood that an index of 71.4 will not tell whether the head is abnormally long or abnormally narrow. It is an advantage, therefore, always to include the average length and breadth of a series as well as the cranial index.

A skull with a cranial index of less than 75.0 is said to be long headed or dolichocephalic ; from 75.0 to 79.9 (inclusive), medium headed or mesaticephalic, while skulls of 80.0 and over are called short headed, round headed or brachycephalic.

The Cranial Index is often spoken of as the " Anthropologist's Sheet Anchor," and certainly is a very useful, rough and ready, preliminary test of race, so far as it goes, but it is only a preliminary test.   On looking at the series of Long Barrow skulls from the front in the foregoing Figs. (1 to 5) one is struck by the repellent look which they have, even for skulls ; a nasty, " hang dog " expression which, when we come to look into it, is seen to be caused by the front opening of the orbits being compressed from above downward, as well as by the cheek-bones being wide and prominent. That these characters are detected and disliked by most people makes me think that they are unconsciously associated with unpleasant traits of character ; for almost everyone is a practical though unscientific physiognomist.   However that may be, the characters are worth noting, because we shall have to contrast them with those of other series of skulls later on.

Very often characteristics which fail to strike the eye in looking at a collection of skulls, do so when a composite contour of several is contrasted with that constructed from skulls of another race.   For this reason I have placed such contours of Long Barrow, Anglo-Saxon and eighteenth century

English people side by side (see Fig. 7) ; and now, in addition to splay of the cheek-bones and scowling orbits, we notice that the face of the Long Barrow Folk is shorter and broader than that of the Saxons, and that the shortening is specially

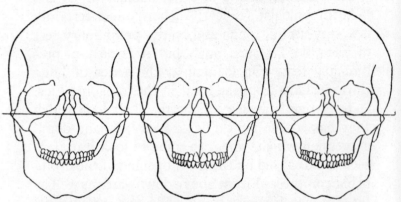

FIG. 7. Composite tracings of 20 Long Barrow, 24 Anglo-Saxon, and 30 eighteenth century Londoners' skulls, showing the difference in the proportions of the upper jaws and orbits.

Long Barrow (20)	Anglo-Saxon (24)	18th century Londoners (30)
Ht. 117 mm.	Ht. 116 mm.	Ht. 114 mm.
Br. 140 mm.	Br. 142 mm.	Br. 142 mm

marked where the roots of the teeth are. The shape of the brain case, too, is different ; for instead of being convex, like that of the Saxon, it is flattened on each side, giving the impression that it is comparatively ill filled.

Speaking of the teeth leads us to look at them, and here I think a useful point may be noted ; for sometimes they are ground flat, as are always those of Anglo-Saxons and Mediæval English, while in other cases they show all the cusps as plainly as they are shown in people of to-day. The probable explanation of this is that when the Long Barrow Folk first came to this country they were a pastoral people, living largely on flesh and milk ; but

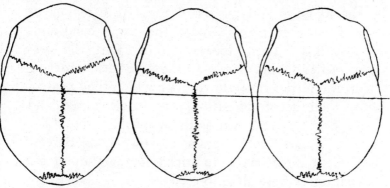

FIG 8. Composite tracings, taken from above, of the skulls of 20 Long Barrow folk, 30 eighteenth century Londoners and 27 Anglo-Saxons. The horizontal line passes through the middle of the ear passages.

Long Barrow (20)	18th Century Londoners (30)	Anglo-Saxons (27)
L. 196	L. 188	L. 192
Br. 140	Br. 142	Br. 143

that, during their stay, the knowledge of cereals reached them and they became agriculturists, grinding their corn in sandstone querns and in this way mixing it with a certain amount of grit which rapidly wore flat the surfaces of the teeth.

The foregoing are facts about the physical characters of this people which we may claim to know from direct observation, but there are others which we may infer. For instance we believe that they were black haired and dark eyed with a swarthy skin, deeply pigmented in certain parts. This is not altogether a gratuitous assumption, for it applies to by far the greater part of Mankind, indeed to all that part which has not been subjected to a special bleaching process among the marshes and forests of the Baltic region, or a few other places where the same conditions prevailed. Then, too, we know that the descendents of this people, in the countries bordering on the Mediterranean, through which they passed, in their great migration, are black haired and dark eyed and, since these people show the same skeletal characters as our own Long Barrow Folk, it is reasonable to infer that their superficial characters were alike too.

Another way of looking at the matter is to realize that there is a dark element in our population which increases from East to West, and is most marked in Cornwall and Wales. Since we know that most of our later immigrants have been of the Nordic Stock, and therefore fair, we must look for the dark strain among the earlier of them, of which the Long Barrow Stock certainly formed a very large part.

It is important that the migration of a People such as that of the Mediterranean Race should not be thought of as an act accomplished in a few years : it was almost certainly a very gradual process, and probably went on for centuries, tribe succeeding tribe, with slight differences of

customs, language and appearance. It is, therefore, no surprise to find difference of custom in
building the long barrows, some being chambered,
like the great one at Rodmarton, while others
have only one central cell for the remains.

The great mass of the Mediterranean Race was,
and still is, straight haired, but a tribal difference
of appearance is described by Tacitus who says
that the Silures of South Wales were dark, with
black, curly hair. Probably he was accurate in
using the adjective " curly," since it is one which
would not be used without definite cause,
though curly haired people do not seem common
to-day in South Wales. They are found, however,
on the south coast of Devon and Cornwall and
possibly may show negroid affinities, gathered
on the southern shores of the Mediterranean.

It is often held that the inhabitants of the
Forest of Dean are fairly pure remnants of the
Long Barrow Folk, and anyone attending a
meeting of the forest miners at the Speech House
therein will be struck by the number of small,
dark people of excitable manners and great
talkativeness. Many of them, too, show the
high cheek bones and beetling brows characteristic of the skulls already shown. That the
nigrescence of the Forest is high I can state from
first hand knowledge, since I have worked through
the people employed at most of the mines, and
have satisfied myself that this character increases
as the neighbourhood of the great southern road

which leads from Lydney to South Wales is left behind. The guide books to the Forest say that curly, black hair is common among the inhabitants, but this I failed to find. Indeed, among some thousands of records, I only found ten or twelve with this characteristic.

In the Rhonda Valley small dark people are common enough, and in the Chiltern Hills, Dartmoor, Romney Marsh and other places it usually is said that pockets of black haired folk are to be met with. Dr. Bradbrooke, of Fenny Stratford, who knew the people of the Chiltern area well and had special opportunities of examining large numbers of them, tried to locate some of these reputed islets, but was not very successful, since it is getting rather late in the day to hope for an undisturbed population so near London. Still, although the general index of nigrescence was not very high, he found that the percentage of black haired individuals was 10.7, a percentage which is not reached in any part of Great Britain of which we have a record, until we come to the West of England and Wales.* We may, I think, feel pretty sure that whenever a high index of nigrescence in the country parts of England is found, especially if it is accompanied by a very low cranial index, the probable explanation is excess of Long Barrow or Mediterranean blood.

*The Anthropology of the Chiltern Hills. Journ. R. Anthropl. Institute, Vol III, 1922, p. 113.

Having discussed, so far as my knowledge allows, the physical characters of these Long Barrow People, their mental attributes must next be considered. The monuments left by them show that they were clever, well organized, and used to working together ; indeed everything points to their having been communists whose unit was the village commune. They must have been daring and skilful sailors, for they reached all the islands of the Mediterranean, and were never found far from the sea shore. They were probably brave enough in warfare, but had been educated by their surroundings of rocks and cliffs to appreciate the advantage of ambushes and surprises over frontal attacks on open ground, and from ambushes to assassination and the stiletto was a natural step for their purer descendents.

People acquire their mental characteristics a good deal from their surroundings, and the continual wanderings of small, weak men, with highly developed powers of imagination, among all the unforeseen and little understood dangers of those early days, must have fostered a sense of cautiousness which soon became suspicion. Then their communism would induce them to see little difference between their own property and that of others, and this, of course, under altered social conditions, led to trickery and petty theft.

It is said that they were revengeful and deliberately cruel, with all the blood lust of the

Southern European reduced to a fine art in Druidism, assuming that Druidism really may be traced to them, and carried down through the ages as Witchcraft. Trickery and deceit, which are the legitimate weapons of defence in small, weak animals, combined with the emotional characteristics of the Southern European, would blossom, naturally enough, into histrionic ability and appreciation of the powers of oratory for which the Mediterranean Peoples, and the Welsh of to-day, are so famed ; while the art of playing upon the emotions by modulating the voice may be the parent of that musical sense which is the birthright of the Welsh, the Irish, and the Highland Scot, and is so much less developed in the more stolid English.

These were the people, so far as we can reconstruct them, who inhabited all that was habitable of our country, from perhaps six to two thousand years ago ; pasturing their flocks on the open downs, hunting in the forests, fishing in the rivers, and celebrating their religious rites in their sacred places. Often they made long journeys from one settlement or shrine to another, for which purpose they marked out definite trackways, along some of which we drive our motors to-day. During the latter part of their occupation they grew corn, and when this was more plentiful than the needs of the growers required, trade began, and made the trackways more needful than ever. These trackways often ran along some low range of hills, as if the travellers were glad to be above the reach of rivers, marshes and floods, and yet wanted to avoid showing themselves against the skyline as far as might be.

Sometimes there were rivers to be crossed, when the trackway would make for some fordable place : and now at last, after wandering so far, we are beginning to sight London, for the lowest point at which the Thames was fordable was at Westminster, to which a trackway, believed to be neolithic, led from the Chilterns and, having crossed the river, ran along the highlands bordering the southern shore of the Thames, to Canterbury and the coast.

Neolithic camps on the Chilterns are common enough, and we have seen that Kent was an important dwelling place of these people. We have seen, too, that agriculture, and probably other arts, were brought into Britain from time to time. It is reasonable, therefore, to assume that the insular Long Barrow Men, good seamen as they were, kept up some touch with their kinsmen on the other side after Britain became an island. Granting, then, that there was a communication between Britain and the Continent, the dwellers in the Midlands would naturally have sought the lowest point at which the Thames was fordable. There are some who believe that the river could be crossed on foot lower down, and that there was a ford at Dowgate but, if this were so, it probably was little used since it is difficult to understand why the original Watling Street, on both sides of the river, heads for miles and miles directly towards Westminster if it meant to turn off suddenly and cross at Dowgate. Again Westminster was, as it still is, a place where the river was broader and therefore shallower than lower down. We cannot assert that the Long Barrow Folk used this ford, but there are reasonable grounds for believing that they did so.

CHAPTER II

THE BEAKER FOLK AND THE COMING OF BRONZE

Some two thousand years before the Christian Era, another race, quite different to that of the Long Barrow Men, made its way into Britain from the Continent : a tall, round headed people which, until lately was known as the Bronze Age Race, because so often its members are found buried with bronze implements ; but since there is reason now to believe that the earliest comers had no bronze, and that the knowledge of it was brought over by later arrivals; they are more aptly spoken of as Beaker Folk, taking their name from the beakers or earthenware cups with which their dead were provided. Sometimes, too, they are called Round Barrow People, after the shape of the barrows under which they buried their dead.

Whence these people came is not known, but since they are found near the Aberdeenshire, Yorkshire and Kentish coasts, it would seem that they must have come from some part of the

Continent far removed from the sea ; and have spread out as they wended their way towards Britain.   Keith traces them to Galicia (J. R. Anthrop. Inst. 1915), while Thurlow Leeds thinks that the beaker which is so characteristic of them was evolved in Spain.

It is thought nowadays that they were not settlers driven Westward by increasing pressure and difficulty in finding food, but visitors in search of the surface gold, which was then to be found in Wales and Ireland.   Having found this, it is believed that many of them returned whence they came, for hoards are often dug up in Kent containing the characteristic work of these people —bracelets, torques and armlets, as well as large numbers of bronze celts and palstaves—buried and forgotten from that day to this.

The gold and bronze articles are so numerous in these hoards, and so often repetitions of the same pattern, that they suggest consignments on their way to the Continent rather than the private property of a family or tribe.   Another suggestion is that they were the work of some artificer who dwelt on the spot and buried his work as he made it, until the right time came for taking or sending it abroad.   There is one particular collection, known as the Bexley hoard, which is a good illustration of this point.   In it are seventeen gold bracelets, all made to nearly the same pattern, found beneath the floor of some crude hut dwellings, which might have been the

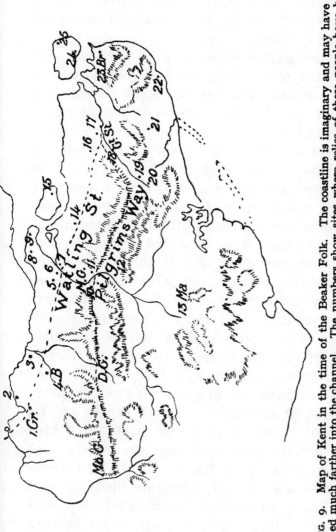

FIG. 9. Map of Kent in the time of the Beaker Folk. The coastline is imaginary and may have extended much farther into the channel. The numbers show sites where relics of these people have been found and their relation to the two old trackways is interesting.

L.—The present site of London.   Gr.—Greenwich.   Ma.—The site of the Marden

Mo.G.—The Dorking Gap in the   B.—Bexley.   Hoard.

     North Downs, through which   D.G.—The Darenth Gap.   Gt. St.—The Great Stour.

     the river Mole runs.   M.G.—The Medway Gap.

workshops where the bracelets were made, or a temporary resting place of the bearers carrying them towards the sea, if the straits of Dover had already appeared.

On the accompanying map of Kent the sites where the relics of the Beaker Folk have been found are marked by figures. Some of these show the position of round barrows, others of buried hoards of bronze implements or of gold ornaments; others again mark burial sites from which the crouching, round headed skeletons have been disinterred, but the interesting point about them for the present purpose, is that the greater number occur near the lines of the two ancient trackways, Watling Street and the Pilgrims' Way, suggesting very strongly that these people were using routes already known when first they came.

The northern track ran straight from Canterbury to the ford at Westminster, and it seems reasonable enough to believe that some at least of the Beaker Folk crossed the river at the former place in their journeys to and from Wales and Ireland ; while those using the Pilgrims' Way were probably going to, or returning from, the copper and tin mines of Cornwall. There seems to have been quite a large settlement of them on the high ground above Greenwich, for, in the park there, only five miles from London, are the remains of some thirty round barrows, situated very close to, if not actually upon, the line of the Watling Street track.

It is not so much the habits of these people which interest us here, as a consideration of how far they modified physically the dwellers in the neighbourhood of the future London. As far as we may judge they seem to have mixed fairly freely with the Long Barrow Folk already living in the country, since long and round skulls often are found in the round barrows. Indeed it looks very much as though the Beaker Folk were craftsmen and traders rather than invaders, and that their main object was to reach the gold and copper regions as peacefully as might be, mixing and intermarrying with the Long Barrow People whenever they were allowed. At the same time there is every reason to believe that they brought their own women with them, since typical, round barrow, female skeletons are quite common, though certainly they are not so plentiful as those of males.

Probably these people were never very numerous in Britain, and, no doubt, many of them went back to the Continent ; though it is clear that all of them did not do so, for Fleure and James have shown how, in certain parts of Wales, there are isolated islands or pockets of broad headed people, living among the hills, which they look upon, justly enough, as remnants of these pioneers surviving until the present day.*

The late Sir William Turner, too, pointed out,†

* *Journ.* R. Anthrop. Inst., Vol. 46, p. 35.
† *Trans.*, R. Soc. of Edinburgh, Vol. 40.

though he generalised upon a small number of observations, that the two counties bordering on the Firth of Forth, Fifeshire and East Lothian or Haddingtonshire, are remarkable for the high

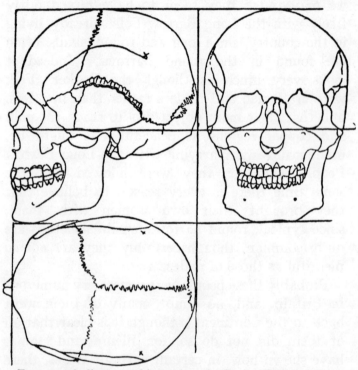

FIG. 10. A dioptographic tracing of a Beaker Folk man from Yorkshire. The broad, round head, rugged features and massive square jaw are quite characteristic.

cephalic index of their inhabitants, and this may mean that the Firth was a favourite point for incoming or outgoing Beaker Folk.

In spite, however, of these patches of broad-headedness, the Beaker Folk did not do much, though they certainly did something, to modify the length of the skull of the Modern Englishman, which still remains longer and narrower than that of any other country in Europe.

Here, perhaps, it may be as well to consider for a moment the value of the Cranial Index, this " sheet anchor " of the anthropologist as it is called. Sir William Flinders Petrie* has stated his belief that it is a phenomenon due rather to climatic conditions or isotherms than to race. To illustrate this he has quoted, I think quite accurately, the case of Lombardy, which was overrun by the Lombards, a long headed, Nordic Race, in A.D.568 and the result of twelve hundred years of changed environment has been to convert Lombardy from one of the longest, to one of the shortest headed regions of Europe. I cannot help thinking that, in his enthusiasm, Petrie has left out facts which should be considered before any judgment is passed. What he has not laid any stress upon is that Lombardy, like the rest of the North of Italy, is very close to the Alps, which were the centre of the short headed, Alpine Race, the second of the three great European Races or Stocks, of which the Mediterranean Race was the first.

Another thing which he has not pointed out is that the Alpine Race is one which, during the

*Migrations. Journ. R. Anthrop. Inst., Vol. 36. (Huxley Lecture for 1906.)

last twelve hundred years, has steadily been spreading, and swamping its long headed neighbours both to the North and to the South of its Alpine home. Doubtless he would be ready to admit that, in the early years of the Christian Era,

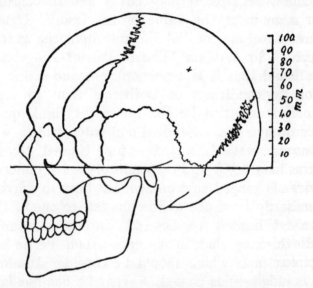

FIG. 11. A composite tracing of the profiles of fifteen male Beaker Folk skulls, the average length of which is 184 mm. and the height above the top of the ear passage 117 mm.

Germany was occupied largely by long headed Nordic tribes; yet to-day almost the whole of Germany has quite a high cephalic index. No one who served in the late war would describe his enemies as a long headed people; while the large number of German prisoners of war in this country at that time enabled Mr. Le Gros Clark and myself to take definite measurements of soldiers coming from every province of Germany,[†] and to show that, while the south eastern provinces, such as Bavaria and Silesia, gave us cephalic indices between 84.0 and 85.0, even Schleswig Holstein and Oldenburg,whence came so many of our own long headed Anglo Saxon forefathers, are now inhabited by people with a cephalic index of over 80.0.

This does not look hopeful for Petrie's contention that it is the climate of the " long headed North " which changes short heads into long ; nor does it induce us to place much faith in his converse argument that the " short headed South " turns long heads into short, even if we had not the evidence of the long headed Mediterranean Race persisting unchanged in all the southern parts of the Mediterranean peninsulas. In common, I believe, with most anthropologists, I am of the opinion that the short headed Alpine Race, unless it is checked by violent means, will in the long run always displace its long headed Nordic neighbours, not because it is a more virile or a cleverer race, but because it is a less expensive one to keep, since it can do its work on smaller rations of oxygen and food, and also because it will breed freely under conditions which the Nordic will not tolerate. It is not quite the case of the grey squirrel ousting the red, or of the

[†] *Anthropological Observations on German Prisoners of War.* **Journ.** R. Anthrop. Inst., Vol. XLIX.

brown rat replacing the black, because in both these instances the newcomer is a larger and stronger animal than the older inhabitant.

Perhaps a truer simile would be to imagine a colony of elephants inhabiting a certain region, to which a colony of rabbits had access. Given enough time, the rabbits would have increased

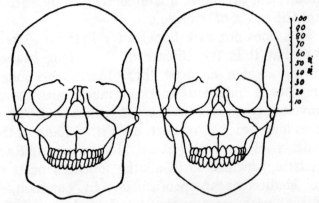

FIG. 12. A comparison of the composite facial contours of 7 male Beaker Folk (left) and 30 male modern Europeans of the Alpine Race (right). The great difference in the jaws will be noticed.

enormously, and would have eaten all new vegetation to such an extent that the elephants would either have starved or have moved away in disgust. A visitor to the spot where elephants were known to have dwelt would find, then, only rabbits ; yet he would never think of suggesting that the elephants had turned into rabbits. The latter, however, is what Petrie would have us believe has happened in the case of the Lombards ; for, starting with a long headed population and finishing with a short, he says " See how climatic conditions have changed these Dolichocephals into Brachycephals," rather than " See how the Brachycephals have survived and multiplied under conditions of overcrowding, which no Nordic People could endure." The question then natu-

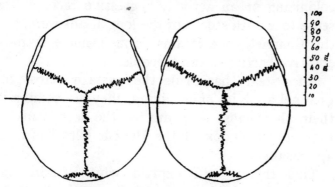

FIG. 13. A comparison of the composite tracings of the upper views of the skulls of 8 male Beaker Folk (right) with those of 30 male modern Europeans of the Alpine Race (left).

rally arises " Why has not the Alpine Race crowded out the long headed stocks in Britain?" I believe that the answer is " Because of the sea."

The men of the Mediterranean Race were good sailors, and, as we have seen, always kept near the sea ; while my later pages will prove abundantly that the Nordic Race loved the sea, and courted its dangers from a sheer spirit of adventure. The Alpines, on the other hand, made for the barren highlands of the centre of Europe ; though whether because they liked mountains, or because, being later arrivals, they found the lowlands already occupied, I do not know. From these regions they spread slowly but surely, like the flowing tide, into the neighbouring lands, until the sea was reached in certain places ; although, having reached it, they made few attempts to embark upon it. They were not a colonizing or an actively aggressive race, in the sense that both stocks of the long heads were, and the Channel, once it was formed, made a most effective barrier to these people.

Since steam has made the passage across the Channel a trivial undertaking, they are coming in their thousands, and during the last century, the cephalic index of the British Isles has risen appreciably.

This theory will explain why Britain was prevented for so long from being gradually over-run by the short headed race, as Germany has been ; and it is quite in harmony with what we know of the incursions of the Beaker Folk, who well may have come here before the critical time of land depression or sea elevation about 1800 B.C. At that date it seems likely that the main mass of the Alpines had not reached as far westward as the present continental coast line ; and we may look upon the Beaker Folk as an advanced guard which having interbred with Nordics, had acquired some of the mental traits of the latter people, one of which was the wish to break away from the herd in search of profit and adventure. Thus we see what a great event was this sinking of the last land link between Britain and the Continent ; and how, but for it, the long headed Englishman of to-day would almost certainly have disappeared.

Skeletons of the Beaker Folk have been dug up in Aberdeenshire, Yorkshire, Kent, Wiltshire and Dorsetshire, and specimens of their skulls are to be found in many local museums. Formerly they were regarded as singularly tall men, and whence and how this height had been gained was a puzzle. Probably many of the burials in the round barrows were those of chieftains who had won their rank through their bodily stature and strength, but in any case the more careful measurements made in the last few years point to the average height of the males being not much above 5ft. 7in. or 5ft. 8in. though that was a good deal taller than the average of the Long Barrow Men. They were certainly of a more robust and stronger build, and agreed in everything except height with the Alpine Race on the Continent to-day, which is heavy, thicknecked and powerful. The reputed height of these Beaker Folk has induced many anthropologists to believe that they were a mixed race with a good deal of Nordic blood in their veins, but it must be remembered that stature is a character which reacts most rapidly to changed surroundings. Nothing, for instance, is more astonishing than the way in which each generation of modern middle class Englishmen is a little taller than the one which went before it, as education and a knowledge of hygiene becomes wider; and, knowing this, I was not surprised to find that, after an interval of ten years, the average stature of the students at the London School of Medicine for Women was an inch higher than that of their predecessors. I am far from saying that stature is of no value ethnologically, but it seems to vary within wide limits, according as the surroundings are favourable or the reverse, and we yet have to learn where those limits are fixed.

What was the colouration of the Beaker Folk is unknown. It has been said that they were fair haired, but I do not know on what grounds. We do not even know the colouration of the pure Alpine Race, since none of the three great European stocks exists now in a pure state; and every European individual is a patchwork of characters which belong to all three of them. Still the logical conception of most anthropologists is that the original pure Alpine Brachycephal was a man with brown hair and grey eyes, because most of the round headed people of the Alps have that colouration to-day.

Perhaps it may be better to leave this difficult question of colour until the physical characteristics of the third great European Stock, the Nordic, are considered, because more evidence will then be available.

The mental characteristics of the Beaker Folk can only be surmised from a study of the round

headed peoples of Europe, as we know them
to-day, and from their behaviour, as recorded by
History. Perhaps their most marked characteristics are their gregariousness, patience and
persistence. They seem always to have moved
in flocks, pushing their way westward along the
path of least resistance, and seldom breaking
away from the herd until they were surrounded
and cut off by their more energetic neighbours.
Though undoubtedly they could fight bravely
and stubbornly, they always seem to have done
so, either when there was no help for it, or when
they were very likely to win ; and, even then
they were at their best when they had Nordic
leaders or were allied with a Nordic tribe. That
they were content to take the second place and
labour patiently for others is shown by the way
in which the word " slave " has been derived
from the national name Slav. This capacity for
patient drudgery made it easy for them to gain a
foothold in the territory of their Nordic and
Mediterranean neighbours, where, by their greater
fecundity and by the way in which they were able
to survive and work under less favourable conditions, they gradually supplanted their hosts.

Their mental capacity was probably higher at
that time though of a different quality to that of
either of the two other main stocks. In Philo-
sophy and Poetry their descendents have excelled,
though no doubt their patience has enabled them
to follow trains of thought from which the minds

of another race would have been turned aside. In craftsmanship they are not on a level with either of the longheaded races, and this perhaps may be correlated with feeble development of the cerebellar region of the head. Probably their greatest defect is want of individual initiative, as well as want of rapid adaptability to changing conditions. As rulers they are arrogant and overbearing, but in subservience, placid, hardworking and law abiding.

What their original language was is not known, for they seem to have lost it very early and very completely, since they are born linguists and learn any neighbouring language with great ease. The Slavonic speech belongs to the Aryan or Wiro group of language, and almost certainly was the property of the long headed, Nordic people, who, in their countless wanderings and incursions, imposed this Aryan speech upon nearly the whole of Europe, as well as upon a good deal of Southern Asia. Doubtless the short headed Slavs and Alpines picked it up easily enough; perhaps because it was a better language than their own ; perhaps because it was the tongue of a race which, however temporarily, was able to enforce its authority upon any other people with whom it came in contact. It is easy to believe that when the Beaker Folk came into Britain they brought the Celtic language with them, but it does not follow, by any means, that this was their original tongue, and that they had not lately picked it up from neighbours or rulers who spoke it.

It is sometimes said that the only definition of a Celt is that of a man who spoke a Celtic language ; and to most Continental anthropologists the Celts are the round headed races from which the Beaker Folk were largely derived. As will be seen very soon, this view has led to a good deal of misunderstanding between our Continental colleagues and ourselves, and the term, when it must be used, always needs some explanation as to what is meant by it. It will very likely have occurred to the reader that the characteristics outlined for the Alpine Race as a whole do not apply altogether to the Beaker Folk, since the latter broke away from the main herd in small parties ; and if they went to Ireland, may have made four sea voyages ere they returned with their gold. This difficulty may be met by pointing out, on the one hand, that the stimulus was quite exceptional ; that the desire for gold and bronze may have overcome the herd instincts of the more adventurous spirits ; or, on the other hand, it may be thought that this adventurous behaviour is a sign that the Beaker Folk were not pure Alpines, but had a good deal of Nordic admixture. The latter I should be only too willing to grant, since it is quite unlikely that, even in 2000 B.C. there was any large body of pure Alpine people in Europe. Moreover, although the shape of the skulls of Beaker Folk, which I have dug up, or handled in our museums, does not suggest Nordic traits, I cannot help thinking that, when the Nordic and Alpine stocks fuse, the skull shape of the Alpine and the colouration of the Nordic are retained. At least this is the impression which examining a large number of modern German prisoners of war has given me

Otherwise the little that we know of the behaviour of these people in our Islands seems rather to point to their peaceable existence among the Long Barrow Men. At first, no doubt, before they had the copper and tin with which to make their bronze celts and palstaves, they must have fallen victims in many an ambush set by the little dark people; but, once the bronze was theirs and the castings made, they must have been in a position to dictate the terms on which the two races were to live.

That the earlier arrivals of these people in Britain had no bronze is the belief to which most field workers have come. In the Museum of the Royal College of Surgeons, in Lincoln's Inn Fields, is an almost perfect skeleton of a Beaker man which was found in a circular trench at Broadstairs,* where it had been buried in the usual flexed position, with at least eight companions; but, although no one with any experience could doubt for a moment that these were typical Beaker Folk, no bronze implements of any sort

*Bronze Age and Jutish Bones from Broadstairs. Journ. of R. Anthrop. Inst., Vol. 43, 1913, p. 550.

were found with them. This, of course, does not show that they had not the knowledge of bronze and how to make it.

My interpretation of the find, at which I worked for some time, is that a number of them, possibly a large number, had entered Kent, perhaps while Britain was still joined to the Continent : that their entry was prompted by reports of tin, copper and gold to be found in this westernmost peninsula ; that some of them had been killed, possibly in a skirmish with the natives, and that in this case the invaders must have been victorious, since they had ample time in which to bury their dead with due ceremony. Indeed the digging of two large, concentric circles, in the sides of the inner one of which the skeletons were found, suggests a work of considerable time, and was probably carried out while waiting for reinforcements. Whether they raised a round barrow, since removed, we cannot tell, but later on, no doubt, the survivors started on their long journey, and if they took the northern trackway, reached Greenwich in three or four days before crossing the Thames at Lambeth.

I have been told of other circles such as this on the Kentish coast, one at Dover and another at St. Margaret's Bay, but I fear that, if any anthropologist saw them, nothing was put on record. It looks, however, as though East Kent were a recognised landing place for these people, and Kent itself a regular thoroughfare, both on their outward and homeward journeys.

As has been said, it is difficult to realize, from the few facts we have, the relations between the Beaker Folk and the Long Barrow Men, after the former had armed themselves with bronze weapons. The presence in the round barrows of small long skulls makes us think that, on the death of a Beaker Folk chief, some of his Neolithic servants or concubines were slain that they might accompany him into the other world. That these people surely believed in a future state is plain enough, from the special beakers and food vessels with which their dead are furnished.

All this looks as though there were a gradual fusion between the two races, and indeed several skulls have been found which are intermediate in type between the round and long headed varieties. It does not seem, however, that the round-headed people occupied the same position which, as we have seen, they so often did with regard to their Nordic neighbours on the Continent, breeding them out by their superior fecundity and industry. Probably the number of Beaker Folk in the country at any one time was never large ; partly because a great many of them returned to the Continent, and partly because their females were few. It seems much more likely that their possession of bronze, their superior physique, and perhaps their mental characters made them the ruling caste ; that they lived on friendly terms with the Long Barrow People, breeding with the daughters of the latter when their own women were scarce, and, when they were plentiful, forming separate communities, some of which lasted to our own time, as Fleure has shown. In this way a mixed race would have been formed with a cephalic index rather higher than that of the Long Barrow Folk, but nothing like as high as it became in those parts of the Continent where their numbers were so much greater.

The researches of Peake and Fleure suggest that possibly there were two incursions of round headed people, the earlier of which were tall, very dark and particularly thick necked, with short broad faces. They were, Peake thinks, of the same build as the figure on the lid of a stone sarcophagus in the British Museum, and he traces them to Etruria and possibly farther back still, to Babylonia. It is to these people, for whom he suggests the name of " Prospectors," that he credits the introduction of bronze into Britain, as well as the raising of the megaliths and dolmens. It was they, he thinks, who reached the Wicklow Hills, where gold had been worked since 2000 B.C.; and he sees in some of our successful merchants of to-day the same physical characteristics. To me the figure in the British Museum suggests the build of some of the Roman Emperors, who may quite well have had Etruscan ancestors, but I have not as yet been able to identify the type among the successful merchants whom I have seen. It cannot, I think, be said that the " Prospectors," as a distinct element in Britain, have yet been adopted by anthropologists at large, though Peake's suggestions are always worthy of the fullest consideration. The mention of them, however, will serve to show how uncertain our knowledge is of the people who lived here three thousand years ago, and how easily a few more facts may make us recast the whole outline of our story.

We seem to be able to trace the influence of the Beaker Folk only during the early years of their stay, since cremation gradually replaced burial, and thus their later records are lost ; there is, however, every reason to believe that the slight dark people were present in great numbers at the close of the Bronze age period, ready to fuse with the next wave of invaders. Since our interest lies in the neighbourhood of the future London, we may picture the Thames Valley as peopled, at this time, by a small dark race, slightly, but only slightly modified by the round headed people, hunting, fishing, growing corn, making simple pottery, and tending their flocks on the neighbouring hillsides. Undoubtedly their culture had advanced materially in the last few hundred years, since they now had bronze with all its possibilities.

It is likely to have been somewhere about this time that the dug out canoe, which may be seen in the London Museum, plied across the river from the island above Kew Bridge, where a prehistoric camp was situated. It seems impossible that this great oak tree could have been hollowed out as cleanly as it is, leaving a transverse bulkhead in the middle, without the aid of bronze tools. In support of this belief, the late Prof. Rolleston recorded the finding of a somewhat similar canoe with a bronze age burial. Let us hope that the canoe in the museum was fitted with outriggers, otherwise a voyage in it, even across the river, must have been a perilous one. It is quite possible that it was with the help of craft such as this that the Northern Beaker Folk reached this country, since our belief is that they came during the age of land elevation, which seems to have ended about 1800 B.C., during which period Britain was not an island. Dug out canoes would be quite able to cross a broad river, such as the Rhine, with its tributary the Thames, as it flowed North, and would be well suited for swamps and very shallow water.

CHAPTER III

On Colouration and the Coming of
the Celt

About six centuries before the Christian Era, members of the third of the three great European Stocks, the Nordic, began to reach Britain in the shape of the Celtic tribes. This Nordic Stock, as has already been pointed out, is of special interest, owing to its having undergone a bleaching process somewhere near the shores of the Baltic Sea, which led to a loss of pigment in some parts of the body, and a lightening of its hue in others.

This change must not be confounded with the white protective colouration of arctic animals, in which the hair is white from the liberation of minute particles of gas among its cells ; for it is an actual suppression of the black pigment in the hair, of nearly all the pigment of the skin, and of the dark colouring matter in the front of the iris of the eye. Apparently it is not the effect of snow or of the long Arctic nights, because the Eskimo are black haired and dark skinned ; but it should rather be ascribed to a filtering of some particular rays of the sun by foggy or very cloudy surroundings. That it took many ages to accomplish this change is probable ; though, when once it began, it would, no doubt, be aided by sexual selection.

When once fixed, colour seems very permanent, and is a great help to the anthropologist in tracing the origins of various peoples ; indeed some of our greatest authorities say that it is much more to be relied upon than head form, and agree as to the necessity of using some common index of nigrescence. The method which I have adopted is suited to a rapid inspection of large masses of people, all that can be done in many cases, and is founded on the colours of their eyes and hair. When a more leisurely examination can be made, as in a hospital, school or other institution, many more points, such as the tint of the skin and the colour of the short hairs on the back of the wrists, may be noted. The eyes and hair alone, however, give a very good clue to the origin of a population, particularly if the examination be limited to people, all of whose four grandparents lived in the same neighbourhood.

As an example let us suppose that 300 people have been inspected, and their hair and eye colours marked on a card against the following headings in such a way that, on adding them up, these totals and percentages were obtained.

		INDIVIDUALS	PERCENTAGES	
	RED	15	5%	
	FAIR	78	26%	
HAIR	BROWN	126	42%	
	DARK BROWN	72	24%	27
	BLACK	9	3%	
		300	100	
EYES	LIGHT	210	76%	
	INTERMEDIATE	36		24
	DARK	54	24%	
		300	100	51

51 ÷ 2 = 25.5 = Index

So far as the hair goes, the scheme, I think, is easy enough to follow; but in the case of the eyes, I have found so much disagreement among different observers as to what should be considered the border line between light and dark, that the personal equation has been eliminated to a great extent, by placing an intermediate group between the light and dark eyes. The number in this group may now be divided equally between the light and dark, before the percentages are calculated. When this has been done, the percentages of dark brown and black hair and of dark eyes are added together and halved, and in this way an index is obtained which shows the degree of pigmentation in the group or district, as indicated by the hair and eyes.

Of course an index of 25.5, obtained in this way is quite meaningless by itself, and is only useful when it can be contrasted with other results gained in exactly the same way. To enable this to be done I have included a map, prepared some

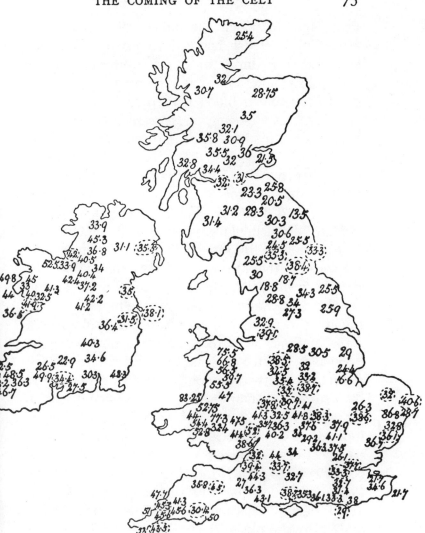

FIG. 14. Map showing the "Index of nigrescence" or darkness of the hair and eyes as it is distributed in the British Isles. It will be noticed that the high figures, showing a dark population, are chiefly in the West. The dotted circles show town dwellers.

years ago, in which the indices of the different areas in the British Isles are recorded. This map shows that an index of 25.5 is quite a low one ; and it also shows how, even to-day, the proportion of Mediterranean blood may roughly be gauged, and how its distribution corresponds with and confirms the modern theories of race movement in Britain. It suggests, too, that the truth lies somewhere between Keith's belief that the Mediterranean Stock is not largely represented in these islands, and that of Maddison Grant that the Modern Englishman is an equal mixture of Nordic and Mediterranean Blood. Anyone caring to consult the original paper,* containing the details from which this map was prepared, will see the importance of checking the index by looking up the records of hair and eyes separately ; for sometimes very dark hair accompanies light eyes, as is so often the case in Ireland.

Another method, which sometimes gives a hint of Mediterranean influence, is to notice the percentage of really black hair in a large number of individuals in any locality. The lists given in the paper already referred to show how rarely this colour reaches 10% ; and then only in the West of England, Wales, parts of the Scottish Highlands and Ireland. This method was used successfully by Dr. Bradbrooke in the Chiltern Area (See p. 44).

Eye colouration makes an interesting study,

*The Colour Index of the British Isles.   Journ. R. Anthrop. Inst. Vol. 50, 1920, p. 159.

but needs a little knowledge of anatomy to understand.   The coloured part of the eye, which surrounds the pupil, is known as the iris, and contains muscle fibres which enable it to act in the same way as the diaphragm of a camera, by contracting or dilating the pupil according to the amount of light passing through it. With these muscle fibres are very many blood vessels, which, when there is no pigment at all, make the pink eye of the Albino. But usually, at the back of the iris, there is a layer of black pigment which keeps the light from penetrating the shutter ; and in the greater number of English children at birth, the eyes have a characteristic leaden blue colouring, owing to this dark layer showing through the more superficial structures.   In most cases, after a few weeks, or sometimes after a few days, a rim of white pigment appears round the edge of the pupil, which gradually spreads over the iris, except at its outer margin.   This white colouring, sometimes only in the form of a ring, sometimes in radiating streaks, sometimes marbled or diffusely scattered, lightens the leaden hue of the new born eye, and the child becomes, and may remain, blue eyed.

Often, however, the white pigment is succeeded by still more pigment of a light yellow hue, and that in turn by darker yellow, and that again by red brown, brown and black ; each colour appearing first at the pupillary margin, and gradually spreading outward ; blending with or obscuring its predecessor to such an extent that no one, casually glancing at another's eye and noticing that it is hazel, would have any idea of the kaleidoscopic patterns to be seen on close investigation. And yet in every eye, the possessor of which owns much Nordic blood, however dark the eye may be, there will be seen a blue circle round the outer margin of the iris, over which the brown superficial pigment has not spread.

In the true Nordic eye the posterior black pigment is there, as it is in all eyes at birth, but the more superficial pigment is very scanty and is limited to the white, with perhaps a trace of yellow round the pupillary margin, thus forming the blue or steel grey eye so characteristic of the stock.

So far as we know, with the exception of some reported but imperfectly examined natives of islands off the western coast of America, it is only the race which has gone through an existence in the Baltic region, where the light rays were modified, though they may not be so now, which has lost the dark pigment giving brown eyes and dark hair. For this reason, I am inclined to think that the original Alpine Race had not grey eyes and brown hair, but rather the brown eyes and black hair, which are so characteristic of all mankind with the exception of the Nordics. It seems more likely to my mind that the brown hair and grey eyes, so often seen in the Alps, are the result of crossing with the Nordic strain, because the character of blondness, once fixed, is difficult to eliminate, even when the fair race settles itself in the Tropics ; and, as we have seen, the light eyes are more persistent and dominant in their heredity than is the fair hair. People with light eyes and dark hair are common enough ; though fair hair with dark eyes is a rarity except in children. When talking of hair colour, the little understood characteristic of red hair always crops up. That, usually, it is associated with a singularly unpigmented, clear skin is common knowledge, and certainly, in more than 75 per cent. of all cases, it accompanies light eyes ; hence it often is regarded as a variant of fair hair, which is particularly well nourished, since it resists the whitening effects of time better than any other colour. On the other hand it has been pointed out that black hair contains two pigments, black and red ; of which the former is fairly easily extracted.

It is curious how often, in collections of mediæval skulls, like those at Hythe and Rothwell, a few hairs remain, and these are so often red that the great novelist, Whyte Melville, advanced the daring suggestion that the skulls at the latter place must have been those of Danes, because he found so much red hair clinging to them. Now, however, it is known that black and dark brown hair usually turn red many years after the death of their owner, owing to the greater permanence of the red pigment. It has therefore been thought that populations in which the proportion of red hair rises much above 5% are possibly mixtures of very fair and very dark races, and that the red haired individuals are really black haired, in which the black pigment has been suppressed while the red remains. The whole subject, however, is receiving a good deal of attention, both from the physical and psychological sides.

The absence of pigment in the skin of the Nordic Race is very noticeable, and one result is that the blue veins show plainly through the clear skin on the front of the forearms and backs of the hands, thus explaining the Spanish epithet of " blue blooded," originally indicating aristocratic or Gothic descent. We do not know exactly what a pure Nordic skull was like, since all our material is more or less mixed, but the late Prof. Retzius in his great work, "Crania Suesica," has left us a most valuable series of photographs of Swedish skulls, belonging to the stone, bronze and iron ages. He has added very much to the value of the work by giving measurements with which to check the perspective effects of the camera, for, without measurements, photographs of skulls may be most misleading. With the information gained from Retzius, and from a large series of dioptographic contours, at present unpublished, of Anglo-Saxon skulls from all over England, which I have collected during the last twenty years, I may venture to call attention to some of the points which seem to be characteristic of the Nordic skull.

The point about the Swedish skulls, which

strikes one at once is that they are not all long
headed, even in the stone age, though by far the
greater number of them are.   Whether this proves
that, even at that early time, members of the round
headed race had made their way to the then
farthest habitable North ; or whether it shows that
the Nordic Race, even at its purest, was never one
in which all its members were long headed, is a
question which should be kept in mind if it cannot
be answered now.   Broadly speaking, however,
the two collections of Nordic skulls have many
points in common, in which they differ from those
of the Mediterraneans.   The technical points would
be out of place here, but some of the main differences will easily be grasped by the lay reader.
Already some of these have been dealt with in
discussing the Mediterranean skull (see p. 40),
especially from the facial aspect.   When viewed
from above, the Nordic skull has a more flask
shaped outline than has the Mediterranean, in
which the sides are straighter and more parallel
and the same thing has been noticed already when
viewed from the front ; giving the impression
that the Nordic skull is the better filled and the
more bulging of the two.   Then, although there
are exceptions, the brow ridges are less well
marked in the Nordic skull, and this gives an
appearance of smoothness in the forehead region,
even in the males, and suggest a womanish or
childish countenance.   Indeed, were it not for the
grave furniture found with it, I should often have

mistaken a male Saxon's skull for that of a female.

The orbits, too, are squarer in their openings in the Nordics ; that is to say their vertical axes are higher, and their transverse axes less broad. This deepening of the orbit, from above down would naturally mean a longer face in any case, but the face is further lengthened by the greater space

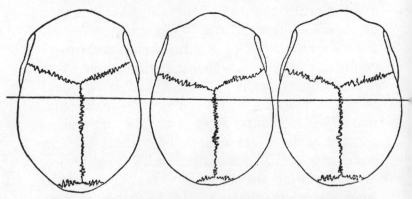

FIG 15. Composite tracings, taken from above, of the skulls of 20 Long Barrow folk, 30 18th century Londoners and 27 Anglo-Saxons. The horizontal line passes through the middle of the ear passages.

Long Barrow (20)	18th Century Londoners (30)	Anglo-Saxons (27)
L. 196	L. 188	L. 192.
Br. 140	Br. 142	Br. 143

between the nasal opening and the tooth sockets. The whole facial length is made still longer by the more massive lower jaw and chin region. This long face, so often seen in pure bred Nordics, and so frequently associated with " character," is sometimes caricatured by Continental draughtsmen, though they may not mean the act to convey a certain subtle flattery.

In the side view of the skull the temporal fossa, where the great biting, or temporal muscle rises, is larger in the Long Barrow skull than in

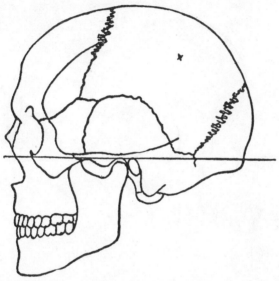

FIG. 16. A composite tracing of the profiles of 27 male, Anglo-Saxon skulls, the average length of which is 192 mm. and the height above the top of the ear passage 116 mm.

the Nordic, and, seemingly, it is this muscle which causes the pushing forward of the cheek bones. Then the ramus of the jaw, as that part is called which hinges on to the skull and bears no teeth, is high, and narrow from before backward in the Nordic, contrasting with the wide and low ramus of the Mediterranean, and this greater width gives more room for the insertion of the great grinding, or masseter, muscle.

It is impossible to attempt here a discussion as to how the head shapes of the Mediterranean, Nordic and Alpine Races have been evolved from

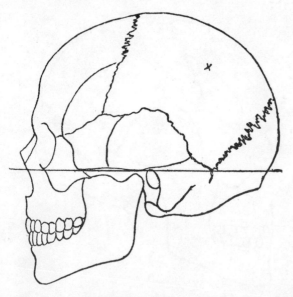

FIG. 17. A composite tracing of the profiles of 20 male Long Barrow skulls, the average length of which is 196 mm. and the height above the top of the ear passage 117 mm.

one another, and as to which is the more primitive type. Some mechanical influence there must have been ; and some craniologists think that these masticatory muscles played no unimportant part in the process. Whatever may have been the factors at work, their influence, once exerted, is very permanent, and we see wonderfully few signs

of change in the English skull between the fifth and
the eighteenth centuries. Moreover the round
head remains unaltered, whether it migrates from
its Alpine home, Southward into Lombardy, or
Northward into Oldenberg.

A well known American anthropologist asserted
that newcomers of various stocks and nationalities
acquire the American characteristics in a generation or two, and resemble North American Indians
in many physical features. His conclusions
though they are not endorsed by the greater
number of his American colleagues, have found
their way largely into popular literature, and are
very welcome to those who believe that there is
little permanence in racial characters. It is therefore only just to mention them here ; though,
before accepting them, it is necessary to know
what proportion the offspring of new settlers,
which shows this American likeness, bears to the
offspring in which no such change takes place.
With almost unlimited material, it is easy to pick
out positive evidence in support of any theory,
and this may lead to a wrong conclusion, unless
the evidence on the other side is weighed.

Not only are the colour and skull characteristics
marked in the Nordics, but there are facial points
worth notice. The nose, for instance, is well
marked and compressed from side to side ; without that splay of the nostrils which commonly is
found in other races. The bridge, too, is prominent, giving the aquiline features and keenness of

expression so often seen in the upper class English man. Indeed I have lately been more and more struck with the way in which the Nordic characteristics seem to be increasing in the upper middle class English youths who come under my observation. In height, colour, long faces, Norman noses and marked chins, they all appear more Nordic than their fathers, many of whom I remember teaching too. The only change seems to be that their heads are higher. The Nordic nose usually has a slight concavity at the root, a convexity at the bridge, and a slight concavity again above the tip. Every transition between this cleanly cut organ and the shapeless, india-rubber like nose, which is commonest among the Alpine and Mediterranean Races, may be met in the streets of London to-day, though some convexity of the bridge is found in more than half the males. This proportion is much higher than among modern Germans, and is quite distinct from the perfect convexity of the Semitic nose with its prominent alæ.

Psychologically, the Nordic Race is probably not the equal of the Alpine in its power of, or liking for, concentrated and prolonged thought ; nor has it the refined taste and sense of beauty in Art or Music of either of the other two great European stocks. It is not fluent in speech, and produces few great orators, so far as may be judged from the present nationalities in which it is preponderant. The commanding and widespread

place which it has won in the world must be due to
other characteristics than these ; more than
anything, I think, to the initiative and adaptability
which each individual possesses, enabling him to
appreciate the movements of the man by his side,
and so to adapt his own movements that as little
confusion as possible results.

In summing up the Nordic mentality, it is
important not to be led too far by the behaviour of
modern Englishmen in the mass, especially as contrasted with that of modern Irishmen ; for both
are mixtures, though in very different proportions,
of Nordic and Mediterranean elements. It is
wiser to think of the records of the Saxons, Norse,
Goths and Danes in the migration days, when
they were comparatively pure Nordics ; and to
realise the wonderful, lightning like swoops which
they made all over Europe under chosen leaders.
Many of these incursions have been mapped for us
in a diagrammatic form by Maddison Grant,*
whose illustration I have adopted with slight modi-
fication, since it shows how continuous was their
wish to push out fresh war bands in every direction away from the barren North.

These were not the steady rolling waves of
people driven forward by hunger and overcrowding, as were those of the Alpines and Mediterraneans ; nor had they for their object the estab-
lishment of trading colonies, such as the Phœnicians founded. They were bands of eager
warriors, ready to meet whatever Fate had in

*The Passing of the Great Race.

EXPLANATION OF FIG. 18. In this map, which is somewhat modified from one prepared by Maddison Grant (see the " Passing of the Great Race "), the wavy lines indicate the area occupied by the earlier Nordics or, as he calls them, Proto-Nordics.

From these the Celtiberians (1) the Gauls (2), the Umbrians and Oscans (3), the Achæans and Dorians (4), and the Phrygians (5), broke away and invaded the south, while the Goidelic and Brythonic Celts (6 and 7) came west into Britain.

The later Nordics, who comprised the High and Low German, as well as the Scandinavian tribes, inhabited at one time the area shaded by straight, vertical lines, marked 8. From these people there were many eruptions at the time of the " migration of the nations "; the most important of which, from an English point of view, were those of the Angles, Saxons and Jutes (marked 9). Later on the Norse (10) and Danish (11) Viking fleets attacked the British Isles on all sides, and also penetrated the Mediterranean as far as Greece.

The area of the Alpine Race, in the centre of Europe, is shaded with small circles, while that of the Mediterranean Race is dotted.

store for them, delighting in the certainty of
difficulties and dangers awaiting them, and sure
enough that they would be able to meet and overcome them. To me they are sanguine sportsmen,
urged on in their forays as much by the excitement
which they derived from them, as by discontent
with their life in the North, or by merely sordid
craving for plunder. Another point which is
worth noticing, is that the number and independence of these migrations show that able and
trustworthy leaders, gifted with that influence
which ensures willing followers, must have been
very plentiful. Thus, not only was the general
average of the Nordics in energy and manhood
above that of the other two stocks, but they also
produced a greater proportion of men with the
rare quality of leadership.

The earliest Nordics, after their bleaching
process in the Baltic Area, seem to have spread
southward over the marshy and open region of
North Germany. At first they were in the Stone
Age of culture, then in the Bronze Age, and later
became acquainted with iron. Retzius gives us
photographs of their skulls in all these periods ;
photographs which are worthy of more careful
study than hitherto they have earned in this country, though it is not certain whether these people
first came to Britain in the Bronze or in the Iron
Age. Peake, who has worked so hard and so successfully at records of the early spread of culture in
these islands, suggests that the handy, leaf shaped,

bronze swords, often found in the Thames, which are on view in the British, Guildhall, London and Kingston Museums, were wielded by the early Nordic leaders, and were improvements on the palstaves and celts which the Beaker Folk used. Unfortunately, up to this time, no skulls have been found with these swords, and thus it is difficult to confirm Peake's suggestion.

The first wave of Nordics or Proto-Nordics, as they are sometimes called, which reached this country, was known as that of the Goidels or Gaels ; and the same name, probably, is handed down in the French word Gauls. If they were in the Bronze stage of culture, as Peake suggests, they had gained it no doubt from the Alpine tribes, north of the Alps, with which they had come in contact. Their real activities, however, seem to have started as soon as they had gained a knowledge of iron, which they did from the same source, and from a culture associated with the finds at Hallstatt in the Austrian Tyrol, a culture which flourished there from about 1600 to 1000 B.C., though in Britain it was a good deal later. These Goidels, we believe, spoke a Gaelic tongue closely resembling the native dialects still used in Ireland, the Isle of Man, and the Highlands of Scotland ; a tongue which possibly had separated from the Proto-Nordic, Aryan language before Latin and Greek were differentiated from it.

It is usually thought that the Goidels came to Britain about 800 B.C., and many hold that their

influence in what is now England was very slight,
though a further study of the leaf shaped swords
of the Thames Valley may cause this view to be
modified. The Erse and Gaelic languages abound
in guttural K and Q sounds, where the later
Celtic wave used the labials P and B : Mac, for
instance, is Gaelic for a son or descendent, as in
MacLeod or McDermot ; while, to the later
Briton, Map or Mab would have meant the same.
Later on the M was suppressed, and the patrony-
mic was merely expressed by Ap, as in ApRice, to
be shortened still further to Price. That the
Goidels, however, must have exercised some influence in England, though it were only for a time,
is made likely by the presence of two such apparently unconnected words as *whiskey* and *Ux-
bridge*. The former, as is well known, is a con-
traction of *usquebaugh*, an Irish word with the
true Gaelic ring ; while the latter is the site of a
bridge over the river Ux, only twelve miles from
London. *Ux, Usk, Esk, Isca, Exe, Axe* and *Ox* are
all Gaelic equivalents with varying vowel sounds,
signifying water ; while *usquebaugh* means water
of life. If it is a fact that so many streams hand
down Gaelic names, it suggests that the Goidels
were at one time an important element in the
population, not only of Scotland and Ireland,
but of the South of Britain and of the neighbourhood of London. Windle, who is a recognized
authority on the subject, strengthens this belief
by pointing out that the well known stone with

Ogham inscriptions, which was found at Calleva (Silchester), suggests Goidelic connections, since this method of writing seems to have been the property of the Deisi of Southern Ireland. ("The Romans in Britain," p. 135.)

It is not likely that the incursion of these Goidels left very much in the way of physical traits in the South of Britain, since two hundred years after their arrival they were driven North and West by another Celtic horde, the Brythons, Britons or Pridans, a name which simply meant painted, tattooed or, perhaps, woad stained people. It is always well to try to find out, not only the name by which a people were called, but what they called themselves, though in many cases, when they were without written records, the former is the only one which survives. In this case they called themselves Cymry, as indeed they do still.

The Britons, when they landed here, about 600 B.C., were in the iron stage of culture of the La Tène period, and their language had altered a good deal from that of their forerunners, the Goidels, to the exclusion of the guttural " k " and " q " sounds, and the substitution of the softer " b " and "p" consonants. It is held by many philologists that language was at that time in a very fluid state, changing very rapidly ; and thus it is not improbable that the two people may have been closely akin one to the other. In any case it is commonly agreed that both were offshoots of the restless early Nordic, or Proto-Nordic Stock.

They must have been firmly established when, in about 325 B.C., Pytheas of Marseilles made his exploration to find out whence the Phœnicians obtained their supply of tin, since he speaks of the country as Pridain : though whether the Britons drove any non-assimilated Goidels across the St. George's Channel, or whether these had already wandered there, as many investigators are inclined to think, is uncertain. But the physical characters of the modern Welshman leave us little room to doubt that the Britons mingled readily and freely with the darker Long Barrow Race, and that in all probability the result was a population in which the Mediterranean characteristics were in excess. To the anthropologist it is very important to know what proportion of women and children accompanied the warriors in their wanderings ; and here the testimony of Plutarch* is valuable. In his " Life of Camillus," he says " The Gauls came of the Celtae, whose country, not being able to maintain the multitude of them, they were driven to go and seek other countries to dwell in ; and there were among them many thousands of young men fit for service and good soldiers, but yet more of women and little children." This account is quite in harmony with what we find in Britain ; for had they not brought their women folk in ample numbers, their physical and mental characteristics would quickly have been swamped, and

*Plutarch seems to have obtained his information about these people from Posidonius the Stoic, and Posidonius from Marius, who knew a good deal about them.

there would have been little chance of their
language surviving.

It is not often that the opportunity of examining the remains of these people occurs, since

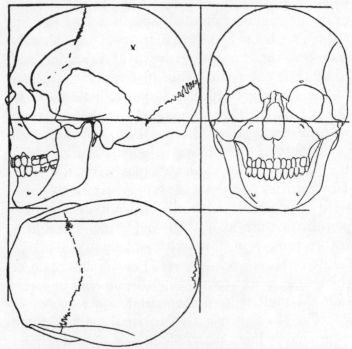

FIG. 19. A dioptographic tracing of a Romano-British skull
from Frilford.   It shows all the Nordic characters.

they burned their dead until some time after
the Romans had been in the country. Thus the
difficulty is to know whether any individual
skull of a Romano-British cemetery is British or
that of some alien race included among the
Roman legions. Even if we could be sure that it

belonged to a native, there would be still the probability of its blending Cymric and Long Barrow features. It is unlikely that the skeletons of Cymric Britons, when first they landed, would be distinguishable from those of Saxons or other Nordic tribes. I venture, however, to reproduce the contours of a Romano-British skull, which Sir Arthur Keith and I believe to be typical of these people. Except for the grave furniture found with it, there would be nothing to enable a craniologist to say that it was not a Saxon skull, since its characters are purely Nordic.

The tendency of modern students is to connect these Brythons, from the very first, with the Cymric Belgae, instead of assuming that the latter people only came into Britain from fifty to a hundred years before Cæsar's arrival. No doubt there was a very large influx of them about this time. Indeed it seems likely that whenever times were bad in Northern Gaul, a number of the Cymry, who were well known to their neighbours as Belgae, moved across the Channel, and that, under other conditions, a movement in the opposite direction was brought about It is, therefore, likely enough that the level of civilisation did not differ very much between Southern Britain and Northern Gaul, during the last four or five centuries before the Christian Era, and it is no surprise to find Posidonius describing the Cornish tin dealers as friendly and willing to trade. Pytheas found wheat grown plentifully in Kent, and threshed in large barns; while the fact that mead was the favourite drink suggests that bee-keeping may have been a common occupation, though wild honey was undoubtedly plentiful.

That their artistic taste was excellent there can be no doubt; for they made beautiful pottery and metal work, ornamented with flowing lines and graceful curves, evidently copied from plants. One of the most striking points about their art is that so often they knew exactly where to stop; for some of their most telling pieces of metal work have only a few bold lines of ornament, yet so arranged as to give the greatest pleasure to the eye. In other words the Celtic Cymry were artists and craftsmen who did not suffer from that dread of blank space, which so often led to an overloading with unnecessary ornamentation of the work of their Teutonic successors.

For a full century before the Romans came the Britons had a gold coinage, copied from the Macedonian stater, which evidently had come into their hands in the course of trade,* but soon lost its original design. There is no doubt that they were skilful weavers, and seem to have been fond of bright colours. In the winter, of course, they wore skins and furs as we do to-day.

This account suggests an industrious, culture seeking, even if not actually civilized people, but

*Elton suggests that these coins were payments for tin, shipped from Thanet, which he identifies with Ictis or Mictis. See *Origins of English History*, Lond. 1882. Other people think that Ictis was the Isle of Wight or Michael's Mount.

they had other less deserving qualities. Their
habit of tattooing themselves was long kept up, and
is usually regarded as a degraded custom, although
to such artists in line as were the Britons, tattooing
must have offered many opportunities. Staining
the body with woad, too, may have been a delibe-
rate war measure to make them less visible, for it is
known that the sails of ships were stained blue with
this object. Druidism, on the other hand, is less
excusable, since it was evidently a cult attended
with horrible cruelties, in which one seems to see
the same pandering to the blood and pain lust of
the Mediterranean Race, which the Roman arena,
the Inquisition and bull fights served so well.
Although Druidism was not confined to Britain
but flourished in parts of Gaul, Britain was
its headquarters, and it is possible that the sacri-
ficial ceremonies were handed down from the Long
Barrow Folk in this country and in Gaul ; or had
spread to Gaul from Britain. There is some evidence that the priestesses of the Cymric tribes,
while they were still on the Continent, used to
kill the prisoners of war, and read auguries from
their internal organs. Apart from this, human
sacrifice does not seem to have been a common
religious exercise among Nordic peoples, though
certainly it was sometimes resorted to, and thus
it seems probable that the habit of torturing their
enemies, which was a failing of the Ancient

Britons, was a remnant of their Mediterranean rather than of their Nordic origin.*

But Druidism had a higher purpose than mere sorcery, and the preservation of a privileged priestly caste. It undertook the training of youth, thereby strengthening its own position, as well as educating the people to a certain limited extent, for we are told that discussions were held on the wonders of Nature and on Astronomy, as well as on spiritual dogmas, such as the doctrine of reincarnation.

Before the Romans came the gods of the Britons were many, and often the same deity was known by several names. As might be expected they were sometimes the same as those worshipped by the other Celtic tribes on the Continent, and it is interesting to find that, with slightly altered names, many of them reappear in Ireland.

The chief god seems to have been Taranis, whose sacred plant was the house leek. Since he controlled the thunder, he corresponded to Jupiter and Thor.

The war god was Belatucador, also known as Cocidius and Camulus, the latter name appearing in Camulodunum (Colchester) and the former, perhaps, in the Welsh surname Tudor. Belisama

---

*Cicero says " it is the greatest pleasure in life to see a brave enemy led off to torture and death." It is quite true that the Saxons in their pirate days often left a tenth part of their captives crucified upon the beach ; but they did it as an offering to their gods, believing that it ensured them a safe return, and not with the intention of gloating over their victims' sufferings, the sight of which would have caused such refined pleasure to the Romans. See Elton, *Origins*, p. 310.

was the British Minerva, but the most popular god seems to have been Belin or Belinus, whose attributes were those of Apollo. Since he was the god of science and learning the druids were his priests and interpreted his commands. His sacred emblem was the mistletoe growing upon the oak, a not very common host for it in these days. This was cut by the archdruid at the beginning of a month, that is to say when the moon was six nights old. Sometimes Belin appears as part of a proper name, as in Cymbeline.

It is interesting to think how the cult of the mistletoe, which was regarded as a panacea for all ills, keeps us in touch with Belin to this day; but many more of the British gods still linger in folklore and fairy tale, and are gradually being identified.

Neptune seems to have been personified by two gods, Nudd and Lud, the former of whom appears also as Nith, Nodons, Nodens, and in Ireland as Nuada of the Silver Hand. At Lydney Park in Gloucestershire he is figured on a pavement tile as a Triton, borne by sea horses; though this probably is a Roman interpretation of him.

Lud, Lug and Lir seem alternative names for the same god, who sometimes appears to be confused with Nudd. He too was connected with the sea; and it has been suggested that Ludgate and Lydney were sites on the great eastern and western estuaries, where seamen might have worshipped or returned thanks to him. The later Welsh historians have incarnated Lud as a king of London, who built the walls of that city; while Shakespeare's play of King Lear was founded upon a traditional tale of Lir, recorded by Geoffrey of Monmouth.

There still remain to be mentioned Mabon or Maponus, a youthful god, who shares with Belin the attributes of Apollo, and the Deae Matres who seem a later addition to the Celtic pantheon and perhaps were more highly esteemed on the Continent than in Britain. These were three goddesses bearing emblems of fertility, like Ceres, and are thought to linger still in folklore as the " three fairies " and the " white ladies," though it is possible that the three fates or Wyrds of the Anglo-Saxons may be the true originals of these.

In addition to these every spring, river and mere had its own deity, such as Sul, Sulis or Suliva at Bath ; Sabern or Sabrina on the Severn, Coventina, &c.* The teachings of such records as we have been able to collect and infer of the last six or seven centuries before the Christian Era, in these Islands, are very instructive from an anthropological point of view. They show the steady addition, layer upon layer, of the Nordic on the Mediterranean stock to form what is now sometimes spoken of as the Celtic fringe. At that time, of course, it had not become a fringe at all, and there can be no doubt that the large in-

---

*A good deal more information about the British gods will be found n Sir Bertram Windle's work, *The Romans in Britain.*

flux of Belgae, which is said to have taken place about 100 B.C., must have made the South East of Britain much more Celtic than were the parts farther North or West. This, of course, is the part of Britain with the inhabitants of which we are most interested, because these are the people, in my opinion, who founded London and are certainly the " Ancient Britons " with whom Cæsar fought, and some of whose habits he has handed down to us in his writings.

" Who exactly were the Ancient Britons ?" is a question which is so often asked that a clean cut, definite answer should be attempted, intelligible to the man who is not a specialist. I will try to answer it in this way. The people whom Cæsar met when he came here in 55 and 54 B.C., were a mixture of the three great European Stocks, Mediterranean, Alpine and Nordic. The Mediterranean characteristics were greatest in the lower classes, and whenever mixed marriages occurred, some of them asserted themselves, owing to their dominance from a Mendelian point of view. The Nordic or Celtic elements were slightly Gaelic, and very largely Cymric or Belgic. All the chiefs, and most of the warriors, were of this race, and probably its characteristics were much more in evidence than those of either of the other two stocks. The Alpine elements were derived from a small residue of the Beaker Folk, who were in the country when the Goidels first came, and also from an almost certain infusion of Alpine or Slav

blood, which the Belgae had contracted in Northern Gaul from neighbouring tribes with whom
they had fought.*

If we could unearth an undoubted collection of
these peoples' skulls, we should know the degree of
round headedness prevailing, and thus estimate
the proportion of Alpine blood, but, unfortunately,
as already has been pointed out, they burnt their
dead and the Romano-British interments are, of
course, a mixture of British and Legionary skulls
which it is impossible to separate now.   At Caer-
went (Venta Silurum), in Monmouthshire, I was
shown a number of skulls and picked out all those
of females which I could recognize, under the impression that they were likely to include more
natives than would be found among the males.   I
was only able to make a cursory inspection, but it
was enough to show that there were a certain
number of broad headed individuals present, with
an index of 80 or more.   Perhaps the same
methods applied to all female Romano-British
skulls may give some results, but two technical
details must not be overlooked.   The first is that
female skulls are known to have a higher index
than those of males, and the second is the puzzling
fact that, even among the purest Nordic skulls to

*In the foregoing account I have simplified the problem as much as
possible.   Every year fresh facts are coming to light which modify
our theories, and would need a very large book indeed in which to
discuss them.   If the reader's interest in the early dwellers in this
country has been aroused, I would refer him to Peake's scholarly work,
The Bronze Age and Celtic World, which reviews all the literature of the
subject down to 1922.   For a more popular survey, Fleure's *Races of
England and Wales* will give the views of one of our recognized authorities on British Anthropology.

which we have access, viz., the Swedish skulls of the Stone Age, a certain small proportion of round heads occur. I am beginning now to doubt whether there ever existed a race or stock in which all the skulls were long ; in which, for some reason, certain members did not develop short and broad heads.

It is disappointing that our craniological knowledge of the Britons is so scanty ; still there is no doubt that a great many of the female skulls, at least, could not be distinguished from those of Anglo-Saxons, and this means that Nordic elements are to the fore.

The colouration of these people would help a great deal if we knew it. They are said to have resembled the Continental Gauls, which suggests that fair hair was common ; we are also told definitely that Boudicca had flowing masses of yellow hair, though, of course, she belonged to the ruling class in which this might be expected. The Welsh historical records, not always accepted by modern historians as very reliable, say that fair hair was prized and envied by the Britons, and an unbiassed statement of this kind is likely to be a popular record containing truth. To my mind it suggests that there was a large dark percentage with which to contrast the fair folk, as indeed there is in Wales to-day.

All classical writers agree that the Gauls were tall men, but they say the same thing about the Saxons, who we know averaged 5ft. 6in. in height in the sixth century. Probably this height impressed the Mediterranean recorders a good deal more than it does the modern Englishman.

During the last century before the Christian Era, and, in all probability, during the two or three which went before it, the Cymric people on this side of the Channel were in close touch with their relatives on the opposite shore, as has already been pointed out ; and carried on a thriving trade in tin, lead, copper, gold, skins, corn and slaves, receiving in exchange pottery, manufactured goods and art products. The Veneti, who lived in Armorica, seem to have been the chief ship owners, though other Gallic and even Roman merchants came across with their wares. Indeed, to the Romans before Cæsar's invasion, Britain appears to have been regarded only as a distant part of Gaul.

As evidence of the close relationship between Britain and Gaul, it may be pointed out that there were Atrebates where Berkshire is now, as well as in Gaul : that there were Parisii in Yorkshire, as well as on the Seine, Menapii in Ireland, and close to Boulogne ; while the Morini in Armorica are believed to have derived their name from the Celtic words *Mor Ynnys*, meaning islanders by the sea, a name suggesting a British origin ; indeed, although we lack the knowledge which would allow us to assert that all these people kept in touch with their namesakes across the water, we know perfectly well that the Atrebates did.

Cæsar, in his Commentaries, says that his chief reason for invading Britain was because the Islanders had given so much help to " our enemies" ; and, in saying this, he rather suggests that, not only had they been in the habit of doing so for some time, but were likely to do so again. Probably, like most men who undertake a big enterprise, he had many motives, and though, no doubt, the glory of Rome was always in his mind, he cannot have failed to see that by adding Britain to the State he must raise his political power in Rome very greatly. Moreover, as Oman points out, he knew that Britain was a rich country, where loot would be plentiful, and from which the sale of a conquered population into slavery would mean money for bribery and vote buying purposes. So he summoned the Gallic merchants who traded with Britain to tell him all they knew about the island, though surely so able a man must have known that all their interests lay in dissuading him from his venture. Apparently he got little information of any value from them, and was led to believe that the copper lay in the middle of the Island, and that the natives were savages of a particularly ferocious type.

Evidently Cæsar thought that much that had been told him needed checking, for he decided upon an exploratory raid in 55 B.C., with an army of about 10,000 men and, before this started, he sent Caius Volusenus to explore the Kentish coast opposite Gessoriacum, the modern Boulogne, where his flotilla lay.

CHAPTER IV

Cæsar and London

The story of Cæsar's rather unfortunate first expedition against this country has had libraries devoted to it, and still the missing details form endless food for discussion. From our point of view his observations on the inhabitants are the only things which matter, and these are all too scanty, since he came into touch with only the Kentish tribes in this his first raid. He found these Cantii forewarned of his coming, and waiting to oppose his landing at Dover, which, then, as now, was the chief port for the Continent, and so surrounded by cliffs that any attempt at a forced disembarkation would have meant great loss of men. Probably he had been told by Volusenus that the cliffs ended a little to the North of the South Foreland, and so, having the tide under him, he ran round to Kingsdown or Walmer. This, at least, is the theory which has received most modern support, though there is hardly a place on the South East coast of England which someone has not suggested as the landing place of Cæsar, and the powerful arguments of a late Astronomer Royal, in favour of another place may not be set aside.

Even though the tide still held, there was nothing to gain by going farther North, unless he knew about the Wantsum at Richborough, where his ships would have been protected from the bad weather which played such havoc with them later on. Most likely, however, he knew nothing about it, and, in any case, he was anxiously expecting his cavalry transports, which were coming from Ambleteuse, but had failed to concentrate with him at or near Dover. It is therefore unlikely that Cæsar went farther than Walmer, which, probably, is the site of the gallant behaviour of the standard bearer of the tenth legion. It was very likely at this place also, that the Britons drove their chariots into the water, and the riders ran along the poles to hurl their javelins at the Romans wading towards them.

The British chariots, like their owners' habits of tattooing and woad staining, seem specially to have impressed Cæsar, who evidently had seen nothing like them among the Continental Cymry. It is thought that the Britons retained their chariots because their horses were such poor little things that they were useless for cavalry purposes; while among the Gauls the breed of horses had been so improved that chariots were no longer in use. Still, small though they may have been, the British horses must have been very perfectly trained to manœuvre the chariots, which, unlike those of the Romans, were open in front and protected behind. Cæsar seems to have been im-

pressed with their effectiveness in the hands
of the Britons, for he notices the disorganization
which the whirr of the wheels and the galloping
horses produced upon troops unused to face them ;
while their skilful use gave the Britons all the
steadiness, combined with mobility, which now
are attained by mounted infantry.

In his story of the rest of the short campaign
Cæsar tells us little more about the Britons than
that he was delighted with their bravery. In the
British records, on the other hand, many details,
usually regarded as later interpolations, are added,
such as that of a secret treaty which a British chief,
named Avarwy, had made with Cæsar, to throw
open the gates of Caer Troya (London) to the con-
queror.   This is only one of many references to
London as Caer Troya,* and to Avarwy, who is
said to have been the son of Lud, a late king of that
town.   Avarwy is sometimes thought to have been
the same person as the traitor Mandubratius, who
is mentioned by Cæsar, though this person evidently was an exiled prince of the Trinobantes.
Still it is pretty clear that he must have had
another name, since that of Mandubratius is the
Latinized form of *Man dub bradwr*, which means
the " Black Traitor," an epithet by which someone
must have referred to him in Cæsar's hearing. It
is very unlikely that a child would have been
given such a name as this by his parents.

*This " Caer Troya " or " Troy Novant " seems to have been a
mis-reading, by Geoffrey of Monmouth, of Trinovantium or Civitas
Trinovantium, referred to again on p. 113.

I only mention this side issue because it is important to show that, when the Welsh triads were put into their present form, there was a belief that London existed in Cæsar's day, and that he was scheming with traitors for its betrayal as though it were a key position in his hoped for conquest of the Island. Later on it will be seen that he took no notice at all of London, and the most reasonable explanation is that it did not exist to be taken notice of.

Before considering Cæsar's second invasion of Britain, it may be well to review what is known of the distribution of the British tribes in the southern part of the Island, since without this knowledge his movements are difficult to follow. By far the most important tribe was that of the Catuvellauni, who inhabited the central part of South Britain, between the Thames and the Welland, covering the modern counties of Bucks, Beds, Herts, Middlesex and Northants. It will be seen that they had no sea coast at all, though it was easy for them to keep in touch with the Continent by means of the trackway which passed through their Capital at Verulam (St. Albans), and then, almost South East for twenty miles, to the site of Westminster, where the Thames was crossed by a ford. After this it passed through the territory of the Cantii, for about seventy miles to Caer Caint (Canterbury), the capital of these people, and then across the Barham Downs to Dover. This was the immemorial track, joining North Wales and Central

FIG. 20. The British tribes at the time of Cæsar's invasion, with some of their main trackways.

Britain with the Continent ; used almost certainly, as we have seen, by the Beaker,* and Long Barrow Folks, and destined, later on, to become the Roman Watling Street. So long as the Cantii were friendly or subject to the Catuvellauni, the position of the latter was a commanding one, for not only did the future Watling Street run through their country, but the precursor of Ermine Street passed North from the ford at Westminster to the land of the Coritani who dwelt in Lincoln-shire.

Across the middle of the Catuvellaunian country ran the Chiltern Hills, at that time, perhaps, bare chalk downs, since the beech trees which now clothe their sides had not then been introduced into Britain. This suggestion is founded upon Cæsar's report that he found no beeches in Britain, but Guest† thinks that possibly he used the word *fagus* to describe the sweet chestnut instead of the beech. Along these hills, though not against the sky line, ran the Icknield Way, a track which the Romans adapted very little. It passed from the Capital of the Iceni (probably pronounced *Ikĕni*) at Caister near Norwich, in the direction of Salisbury, though its western end is uncertain. If a mere surmise be allowed, I would suggest that this Icknield way was an old track from the East of Britain to Stonehenge. In

---

*While I am writing I am told of a Beaker Folk skeleton just found at Dunstable, on this road.

†Origines Celticæ.

addition to these three roads, one of the many
Stane Streets crossed the territory of the Catuvellauni, and Akeman Street ran from Bath and
Cirencester, through Berkhamstead, the high
street of which it still forms, probably through
Verulam, and then through Welwyn, across the
Ermine Street at Broughing. After this it continued on to Camulodunum, thus making a
communication between the capitals of the Catuvellauni and the Trinobantes. In its course it
passed between the northern, fertile, agricultural
area of the Catuvellauni and the southern forest
district.

To the East of the Catuvellauni dwelt the Trinobantes or Trinovantes whose capital was Camulodunum (Colchester), a name apparently compoun-
ded of that of the god Camulus and *dynas*, a fort.
It seems that the Catuvellauni and the Trinobantes
were not on good terms about this time, and that
Mandubratius had been driven from the throne of
his Essex kingdom by the former, to turn a
traitor to Britain, his country, and to offer his help
to Cæsar. This, perhaps, is a rather harsh way of
looking at the matter, for it is possible that
the Trinobantes regarded themselves as a Belgic
tribe, lately settled in the country, and acknowledged no allegiance to Britain as a whole. Mandubratius, therefore, or Avarwy, if that were his
real name, may have considered himself quite
justified in asking Cæsar's help toward restoring
him to his people, who seem to have wanted him

back.   It is a little difficult to define the bound-
aries between the Catuvellauni and Trinobantes,
though it seems certain that the Lea separated
them toward the South.

There are some obscure references in Cæsar to
Civitas Trinobantium, which some think referred
to London, though *Civitas* did not necessarily, nor
even usually, mean to the Romans a city, but
rather an administrative district.   If in this case
it did mean a town, Colchester, or some other
oppidum of the Trinobantes would be a more
likely interpretation ;   failing any clue as to its
position.

To the South the Catuvellauni were well protected by the Thames, which separated them from
the Cantii, and, farther west, from the Atrebates ;   the boundary between these two peoples
being apparently, the Wey. On the West, where
the Thames turns north as its source in the Cots-
wold country is approached, the Atrebates were
still the neighbours of the Catuvellauni, and
separated them from the Dobuni in Gloucestershire.   One other neighbour they had in the
north west, where the Cornavii lived, and Watling
Street passed into what is now Warwickshire.

It will be seen from the foregoing description,
aided by a glance at the map, that the Catuvellauni, although they had no seaboard, occupied a
very central position and could carry on a war,
always on inner lines, against any combination of
surrounding states.   Moreover the passage of at

least five important roads through their country must have given them a great deal of mobility, and, in peace time, have kept them well in touch with everything which was going on in the outer world.   It is no surprise therefore to find that they were the most important tribe in Britain in Cæsar's day.

In dealing with the history of small states and tribes, one cannot help being impressed by the fact that their rise and fall depends much more upon the personal capacity and energy of their rulers, than upon their geographical advantages, and at this time the Catuvellauni were governed by a brave and capable ruler, named Cadwallon, Caswallon or Cassivelaunus ;   about whom, unfortunately, we have few details.   We do know, however, that he had taken an active part in giving moral and material support to the Continental Belgae in resisting Cæsar in Gaul, and had attained a suzerainty over the neighbouring Trinobantes and Cantii.   What his relations with his Western neighbours, the Atrebates, were we do not know ;   though probably they were none too friendly, since Commius, the king of the Continental Atrebates, who also had a great influence in Britain, turned against him and did all he could to help Cæsar.

The fact that Cæsar was preparing a second expedition to invade Britain on a large scale, during the winter of 55 and 54 B.C., was duly reported over here, just as all that happened in

Britain was reported to Cæsar by the adherents of Commius and Mandubratius. Indeed, so serious did the position seem that the chiefs of the various British tribes met and agreed to sink their internecine feuds, and to make Cadwallon their leader. It was this meeting or *gorsedd*, though the term bears a rather different meaning now, which the Welsh Triads describe as taking place in Caer Troya; and, if their reliability were assured there would be no doubt that London existed at that time. Unfortunately, however, the ancient Welsh historical records are of doubtful date, and evidently have been tampered with in mediæval times. Apparently, too, there was a great desire on the part of one or more transcribers to link the history of London with that of Troy, and thus the opportunity of introducing Caer Troya as the site of a meeting, the occurrence of which, though not the place at which it was held, was already known and recorded by Cæsar, was too good to be missed. In any case the unsupported testimony of Welsh records is not accepted by modern historians, and we look in vain for any other evidence that London was ever called Caer Troya, or Troy Novant, in its early days ; or that there was any city at all on its site in 54 B.C. Indeed all the evidence points in the other direction.

According to Napoleon III, Cæsar left Portus Itius (Wissant), for his second invasion of Britain, on July 21st, 54 B.C., with five legions and 2000 horses ; landing, apparently without opposition, at the same spot which he had chosen the year before. With our present knowledge it is difficult to see why he chose this open beach on the Kentish coast once more, when, from the first, the Catuvellaunian capital at Verulam seems to have been his objective ; or why, by prolonging his voyage a little, he should not have left his ships securely in the Wantsum, or have crossed the mouth of the Thames and landed on the Essex coast, in the country of the Trinobantes. Here he would have been among friends who would have given him a secure base and provisions while he was reducing the neighbouring country of the Catuvellauni. Given an easterly wind, he might even have sailed up to Westminster, and have placed himself between the Catuvellauni, waiting for him in Kent, and their capital at Verulam.

It is easy enough to make these suggestions with our present knowledge, but we must remember that, although we know more in some ways now than he did then, Cæsar and his advisers knew a good deal then which we do not now.   The part of Kent near the Wantsum and Richborough is very marshy to-day, and may have been hopeless then ; and the unbuoyed and uncharted sands may have made the Thames Estuary too risky for a great flotilla, with 2,000 horses on board, to attempt. Cæsar, too, evidently was hoping that Mandubratius might have been able to win over many of the tribes to his side.

The Triads suggest that Cæsar had a complete

arrangement with Avarwy, and that the latter
induced the British council to reject Cadwallon's
advice to oppose the landing. As this behaviour
is quite in harmony with that of Mandubratius,
we may, I think, consider it as evidence con-
firmatory of the latter's conduct, for clearly
it is not a mere plagiarism from Cæsar, borrowed
during the middle ages, or why should the traitor
be called Avarwy by the one and Mandubratius by
the other ? The argument of course, rests upon
whether we may identify Avarwy with Mandubratius which, upon the whole, I think we may,
for both Cæsar and the Triads describe the acts of
a single traitor to the British cause, although the
details vary. Caesar's name for this person,
though he did not appreciate it, seems to have
been nothing but an opprobrious epithet, while
the Welsh name of Avarwy must have been
gathered from somewhere, and may quite well
have been handed down by tradition. It is easy
to understand the trained, modern historian's
distrust of the Triads as evidence, on account of
the garbling which they have undergone in the
middle ages, and at the same time to see that they
may contain remnants of folklore which at least
are suggestive.

Twelve miles from the coast Cæsar met the
Britons on a river which, if the distance be correct,
could only have been the Little Stour ; probably at
or near Kingston or Barham. This is the conclusion arrived at by Napoleon III, who followed

Cæsar's campaigns with the greatest care, and he also considers that Cadwallon had chosen the best place for covering Caer Caint, the capital of the Cantii, for which place Cæsar evidently was making. The result of Cæsar's victory in this great battle was that Cadwallon realized that the British foot levies could not withstand the trained infantry of Rome ; and henceforth he contented himself with harrassing the Roman advance by repeated chariot attacks and surprises from the woods, in which, it seems, the Roman cavalry were no match for the charioteers. Cæsar, therefore, after the loss of ten days in repairing his ships which had been shattered by a storm, determined to lead his army to the Thames ; by which, no doubt, he meant to the nearest practicable point at which the river might be crossed, though his transport and commissariat must have caused him infinite trouble.

Oman thinks that he followed the main military road, apparently called, by the Britons *Sarn Gwyddelin* or the Irish Road, which, of course, was the later Watling Street. This would have led him through inhabited and cultivated country where crops might be siezed ; though it meant crossing the Medway at Rochester, an undertaking which should have given Cadwallon another good opportunity for checking him. It may be, however, that Cæsar, instead of following Watling Street, took the alternative route of the Pilgrims' Way along the North Downs, a route which would have kept him clear of the woods, and of chariot surprises to a great extent. If he did this he would have crossed the Medway at Halling, where an ancient ford is believed to have been.

Here he would have been only two or three miles from Aylesford, where some beautiful Celtic pottery and bronze work, ascribed to the last century B.C., has been found and is one of many evidences that the Kentish Britons, with whom Cæsar was fighting, so far from being wild savages, were able to design and appreciate flagons, vases and bronze mounted pails, which would be welcome ornaments in any modern room. From this point he may have followed the track as far as Westerham, from which a well known cross track ran north, through Keston, to join Watling Street at or near the ford at Westminster. At Keston is an extensive earthwork, still known as Cæsar's Camp, though of course the name alone means little, and it must be confessed that the large size as well as the shape of the structure suggests a British, rather than a Roman, origin. Perhaps he adapted this already existing camp to his own purposes, more especially since its presence must have meant good trackways to and from it in various directions.

For my purpose it is not very important to decide on Cæsar's route to the Thames; except that if he had followed Watling Street, it would have led him to the ford at Westminster, close to the site of London; while, by taking the Pilgrims'

Way, he might have struck the river farther west, by one of the north going, cross tracks from that road.   In any case it is pretty clear that if he were transporting large pontoons or "*ships*," as he tells us, in addition to all his other impedimenta, he must have kept to established trackways, and could not have wandered at will through the marshes which lay along the south bank of the Thames, or the dense forest, clothing the rising ground which is now Forest Hill, Richmond Hill and Kingston Hill.

All antiquarians seem agreed that Cæsar did not cross the Thames at Westminster (the lowest practicable ford across the river), though I confess that I do not understand their reasons.   If it is a question of stakes, I think that far too much importance has been placed upon them ; although, since Cæsar tells us that the Britons placed sharpened stakes in the river where he crossed, there can be little doubt that they did so.   What I am doubtful about is that they placed them there on purpose to bar his crossing.   It is true that at Brentford there are indications of piles having been placed along the northern shore of the river for nearly two miles, though few people believe them to date from Cæsar's time.   At Coway Stakes, also, near Halliford, there were stakes fixed across the river and cased in lead, which were visible in Bede's time, though it is pretty certain that Bede never saw them.   Is it likely that the Britons would have wasted valuable time in casing piles with lead for an emergency such as this ? And how would a line of stakes across a river have hindered its crossing by an enemy ? It would undoubtedly have been a help rather than a hindrance. It is quite possible that all the fords were permanently staked in this way, and that the Coway stakes, being cased in lead, lasted longer than the rest ; even for the eight hundred years which passed before Bede wrote about them.

I confess that I do not know why the stakes should have been sharpened, but if the Britons expected to impale Cæsar's boats upon them, they must have been very hopeful people. To be of any use for this purpose, the sharpened ends must needs have been adjusted below the surface of the river with the greatest accuracy ; while, even in its present locked condition, the water level varies very quickly. We do not know how far the tide was felt in Cæsar's day ; but if he crossed in the tidal part, sharpened stakes would hardly have been an obstacle at all, however perfectly they were cased with lead.

If we set the stakes on one side, I cannot see that any good reason has been given for believing that Cæsar took any other than the simplest and most obvious course of following Watling Street to its crossing at Westminster, since any detour to the west meant loss of valuable time in reaching Verulam, his objective. The fact that London was not even mentioned suggests very strongly that then there was no London to mention.

Guest, whose industry in collecting evidence was perhaps greater than his judgment in using it, notices that Halliford and Wallingford are the only two places on the Lower Thames to which the Saxons gave the name of *ford*, for Brentford was a ford across the Brent.   From this he deduces that they were the only places at which the river was fordable ; and this necessarily implies that there was no ford at Westminster.   It is hard to believe this, with the two parts of Watling Street converging upon that point, for, on his evidence, they should have met at Halliford.

The point at which Cæsar crossed the river is for our purposes not the side issue it may seem ; for the nearer he crossed to Westminster, the more impossible would it have been for him utterly to ignore London or Caer Troya, if it existed.   He would at least have mentioned it, and certainly would not have left it in his rear unreduced.

Having crossed the river, in spite of Cadwallon's efforts to prevent him, he hurried on to the capital, or main oppidum of the Catuvellauni, evidently along a definite trackway, for Cadwallon followed his old tactics of appearing suddenly from the neighbouring woods with his chariots, and causing as much annoyance as possible.   It looks very much as if Cæsar were working now along the fore-runner of the Edgware Road, which is what this part of Watling Street is ; and the reasonable presumption seems to be that he followed the same route from Canterbury to St. Albans that everybody then took, or indeed takes now, if he journeys by road.

Some idea of what the Sarn Gwyddelin, or Irish Way of the Britons, was like, before the Romans made it into Watling Street, may be gathered by looking at those parts of the Icknield Way which have not been modernised, and picturing the transport of an army along them ; but when it is suggested that this transport was taken for many miles through forest paths, in order to avoid crossing the river at the usual place, some very distinct advantage is needed to account for it, and in Cæsar's case no advantage is evident.

When Cæsar reached the Catuvellaunian capital, the name of which he does not record, he found it the usual British oppidum, in thick woods, surrounded on three sides by a rampart and abattis, with a marsh on the fourth side. This, although no name is given, answers to Verulam in every detail. He took the place by an assault on two sides, and was pleased to find that it contained a large number of cattle, of which, evidently, he was in sore need.

About this time Mandubratius, who had been sent to his people, the Trinobantes, persuaded them to come over to Cæsar's side, and to send him corn. Indeed it looks as if another week of Cadwallon's tactics would have led to a very serious Roman disaster : but now the Britons could do no more ; for, with the Trinobantes, five other tribes came in, though which they were is not known.

Cadwallon, therefore, gave in, having made a splendid fight. It is true that he made a last attempt by inducing the Kentish kings to attack Cæsar's fleet and naval camp, but they were beaten off, and no doubt the British leader found it impossible to keep his troops in the field any longer.

Cæsar went back to Gaul with a good deal of loot in the shape of slaves, and the promise of tribute, only one instalment of which seems ever to have been paid. Doubtless, too, he had taught the Britons not to interfere in Continental affairs, but otherwise he had done very little, at an enormous cost. He never conquered Britain, but merely made a punitive raid into it. Above all he never mentions London, though if it were there at all, it must have lain in the path of his retreat ; even if he worked round it in advancing upon Verulam. It is true that he does not mention places like Canterbury, Rochester, or Maidstone, which he may or may not have entered, nor does he even give the name of Verulam ; but, according to the Welsh records, Caer Troya was an ancient city at this time, and the seat of a king, as well as the site of the central council which gave Cadwallon his leadership. The failure to mention such a place, lying as it did directly in his line of retreat, if not in his line of advance, in a contemporary account of tested accuracy, must outweigh the assertions of the Welsh historical records, of which no one knows the date, and the accuracy of

which is more than suspect, though some of the
details may be facts more or less truthfully recorded by tradition.

An ingenious attempt to save the situation has
been made in the suggestion that when Cæsar
attacked the capital of the Catuvellauni, it was
not Verulam at all which he attacked, but London.
This means that he went a long way West of London to cross the river; so far that he had a long
march back again on the opposite bank; and then
found a town in the woods with a vallum on three
sides of it, and a marsh on the fourth. Is it con-
ceivable that Cæsar would not have known the
Thames again, or that he should have mistaken it
for a marsh? It may, of course, be suggested
that London at this time was the Catuvellaunian
capital, though the suggestion has little to support
it, since we know that, in the times of Cadwallon's
son and grandson, Verulamium filled that position,
and since Cæsar's description of the place does not
tally with London.

No; however much we may wish to add further
antiquity to the many famous things of which
London justly may be proud, we cannot say that
there is any reliable evidence of its existence
in Cæsar's time. However hardly it goes against
the grain, we must admit that almost all the
reliable facts which are known to us make it
very unlikely that there was a town of any importance at all on its site at that time.

CHAPTER IV

THE BEGINNINGS OF LONDON

Cæsar's departure left Britain in a state of
historical darkness for some time ; a darkness
which the study of coins is clearing up to some
extent. It seems that Cadwallon continued to
rule over the Catuvellauni until 47 B.C., when he
was succeeded by Tasciovanus, who reigned until
A.D.4, and circulated a great deal of money bearing the mint mark of Verulam. Since he reigned
51 years, he must have been an old man when he
died and was succeeded by his more famous son
Cymbeline or Cunobelinus. Before he left Britain,
Cæsar had placed his ally Mandubratius upon the
throne of the Trinobantes, and had told Cadwallon not to interfere with him. Soon afterwards,
however, the rebellion of Vercingetorix in Gaul
must have shown the Catuvellauni that the hands
of Rome were full, and that they might do as they
pleased. One of the results of this feeling of
security was that they attacked and conquered
their old enemies and neighbours, against whom
they naturally had a deep resentment, and it
seems probable that Cymbeline was placed by his

father upon the throne of Mandubratius, at Camulodunum, which was later to become Colchester.*

Cymbeline, or Kimbelin, as no doubt the Britons pronounced it, evidently was one of those born rulers who markedly influence the future of their kingdoms. A man like Alfred, Ethelbert, or Charlemagne, gifted with vision, capacity, patience, courage and, above all, ambition, though, unfortunately, without a chronicler, he gradually extended his rule over the whole of the south east of Britain, for his coins, minted at Colchester, are found from Kent to Gloucester. Why Shakespeare should have chosen him for the hero of a play is a mystery to me, for he knew hardly anything about him, beyond the few details to be gathered from the Elizabethan historian Holingshed. The only place name which appealed to me, in reading this justly neglected play, was Milford Haven ; because it is a doubtful point whether Cymbeline extended his kingdom over South Wales or not : in any case the introduction of Milford Haven may be nothing more than poetic licence, though the coincidence is curious.

Kent and the Atrebatian territory of Berks, Hants and Wilts were probably wrenched from the sons of Commius the Atrebate, who first had helped, and, later, had quarrelled with Cæsar. Cymbeline,

*In the foregoing pages I have spoken of Verulamium and Camulo-dunum as though they were identical with St. Albans and Colchester. This is not strictly true ; since, in each case, the new town is situated at some little distance from the old.

like Ethelbert and Alfred, to whom we have likened him, was not insular in the narrow sense, but broad minded enough to welcome foreign traders and craftsmen who could teach his people new ideas, and saying this is to say that he welcomed the influence of Rome. His coins, all of which were struck at Camulodunum, had Roman, instead of Celtic inscriptions, and sometimes he is described upon them as Cunobelinus *Rex.* Indeed, in all likelihood, he did not think that Rome had conquered Britain, but that his grandfather had defeated Cæsar, and therefore he bore no grudge against the Mistress of the World. Certainly he was always on good terms with Augustus and Tiberius, to whom he sent many embassies.

Although his mint and main residence were at Camulodunum, Verulam must still have remained the centre of his Kingdom, from which all parts could most easily be reached, and towards which so many roads converged. At this time, we may believe, both these oppida were passing from their larval stage of stockaded cattle pens into something more like towns, for there is good evidence that foreign moneyers were coming over to improve the coinage, and it is unlikely that they were the only craftsmen who were welcomed. These people, doubtless, must have taught the Britons something more than how to imitate Roman coins, and we may be pretty certain that a definite market place, with perhaps some muni-

cipal buildings, as well as a royal residence, were
to be found in both towns ; though it is likely that
Verulam, owing to its position on the " Irish
Way," was more advanced as a trading centre
than Camulodunum.

There is no doubt that merchants from Gaul and
from Rome were coming into Britain with their
cargoes of manufactured articles, Samian ware,
wine and, perhaps, eastern spices, to exchange for
the corn, skins, metals and, still probably, slaves,
and that the wares which they brought were
distributed and paid for among themselves by the
coinage which Tasciovanus and Cymbeline had
struck.

Now that there was a definite distributing
centre at Verulam, in the middle of the Catuvellaunian area, merchants would begin to realize
how much time and labour would be saved if
their cargoes could be brought as near to it as
possible by water. Soon they would see that,
by sailing through the Wantsum and up the
Thames, the Irish road might be hit at the
Westminster ford, and the weary porterage
through Kent avoided.

Westminster, however, although it was the site
of the ford across which the most important road in
Britain passed, was by no means a good place for
handling cargo, since the banks of the river were
swampy, while the river itself was wide and shallow, and therefore seriously affected by the tide.
This being so, it was only natural that a better place

should be sought, and the claims of London's site
would have been striking enough. It was only a
mile or two away from the main road : the river
was narrower and the banks more suitable for un-
loading merchandise : the openings of two tributaries, the Fleet and the Walbrook, formed harbours for boats of small draught ; the presence of
two brick earth covered hills made comfortable, dry
sites for dwellings above the malarious marshes,
and the fact that rivers or marshes surrounded
these hills on all sides made them safe against surprise. Moreover, the slight elevation of Overy, on
the opposite bank, as well as the comparative
narrowness of the river, made this the very place
for a bridge in the future.

It may well be asked why all these advantages
had not been recognised long before. The answer,
no doubt, is that, until Verulam became a distributing centre instead of a stockade, the advantages were latent. So long as the Catuvellauni
were merely agriculturists and herdsmen, the
part of their country near the Chilterns appealed
to them most, for that near London was marsh
and forest. Thus Verulam, their oppidum or main
camp, was placed in the northern part of the
forest area in order to be concealed, and at the
same time to be near the fertile open country to
the North of it. When it became really a town,
and the Thames route was opened up to merchants,
the advantages of a river port or suburb were
clear enough, and London's site was seen to be the

only suitable place for a port near Verulam, on the
main road to it.

To those who say that a thriving and ancient
town was there already I can only reply that there
is not a particle of real evidence for this assertion ;
nor was it a good site for anything but a trading
town. Again if, as the Welsh records say, a town
called Caer Troya existed here, why did it change
its name ? The more one thinks over the evidence at one's disposal, the more one feels that
the origin of London was in the early half of
the first century A.D., while Cymbeline was
welcoming everything that came from Rome.
This seems to have been the opinion of the late
Prof. Haverfield,* our greatest authority on
Roman London, for he says " It seems rather to
have sprung to size and prosperity owing to the
influence of Roman traders and its uniquely
convenient position." The point which one would
like to know, but to which at present there is no
clue, is this, Did the merchants wishing to get their
goods to Verulam gradually use and settle London,
or did Cymbeline develop the city, foreseeing, as he
certainly had the brains to do, that this would
make an excellent trading station for the merchants whom he was so anxious to attract ?

Perhaps both may be true. One or more
traders may have pointed out what a good port
the London site would make if it were developed ;
and Cymbeline may have proceeded to develop

*The Roman Occupation of Britain, p. 215.

it by making a short cut to it from the Irish Way, and another track which was later on to become the Vicinal Way of the Romans from his own town of Camulodunum. I am inclined to favour the latter as the more probable explanation, but until fresh evidence appears, or present evidence is better understood, it is reasonable to believe that London began in Cymbeline's time, in Cymbeline's country, and with Cymbeline's active help, since its foundation would have been in harmony with the continuous policy of his long reign.

It may of course be objected that Cymbeline had his capital in Camulodunum, but I cannot think that this is any objection to his developing London. He was a Catuvellaunian by birth, and though he may have liked Camulodunum best as a residence, Verulam was clearly the central trading town of his kingdom until London was ready to take its place. Want of a port was the great drawback to Verulam, and perhaps the fact that Camulodunum was a port made him fix his capital there ; though he soon found, as the Romans found later, that it was too much in a corner to make a good trading capital or even an administrative centre. Verulam, with London as its port, was a much more workable conception, and it is quite likely that Cymbeline spent a good deal of his time in the Catuvellaunian territory both during his father's life and after his death, for in the Chiltern country are two villages, called Great and Little Kimble, the names of which have hardly

changed since Domesday Book was compiled, and
these are held locally to perpetuate his name.

It must not be thought that the distance between Verulam and Camulodunum was great for a
light chariot with relays of horses. It is fairly
certain that there was a British road between the
two places, for the Romans paved the greater
part of it later on, and it is still used as one of the
many Stane Streets. There were few, if any,
obstacles between the two towns, and Cymbeline
or his messengers should have passed from one to
the other in little over five hours, especially as by
this time the breed of horses had probably been
improved.

W. Page (*London: Its Origin and Early Development*) makes an important point of the origin of
London being dependent upon the rise ot Camulodunum rather than upon that of Verulamium.
His suggestion is that Cymbeline, after making the
former place his capital, found that, in order to
keep in touch with the South, he had first to go
to Verulam, and then, along the Irish Way, to
Westminster. The natural remedy was to make a
third side to the triangle, thus connecting Camulodunum with the ford at Westminster. Later on
the advantage of a bridge at London's site, with a
short connecting road between Southwark and the
Irish Way at St. Thomas's Watering, now Brick-
layers' Arms, shortened the route still more.

The difference between this point of view and my
own, which shows London's beginnings as due to

Verulam rather than to Camulodunum, is not very great and depends upon the value which each of us places upon the relative importance of the two towns. To me the central position of Verulam in Cymbeline's kingdom appeals more than the fact that Colchester had lately become the royal city. I am, however, quite willing to admit that there is much to be said upon the other side. All that I would do is to call attention to the way in which every fresh effort to trace the origin of London makes it more and more likely that the founder was Cymbeline.

Possibly more time and ingenuity have been spent over the early origin of London than the facts at our disposal justify. Naturally we would like to know how our city began, and each strives to build up a working hypothesis according to the comparative value which he places upon the various known facts. At present the origin of the name Llyn Dynas is under a cloud, but before rejecting it, one must remember that Celtic Philology is in an uncertain stage, and that its professors seldom see eye to eye, even in translating a simple early Celtic inscription. In any case it is important that stress should be laid upon the fact that London is not a Roman name ; and that even though its first syllable may not be derived from the British " llyn," a lake or mere, no objection has ever been taken to the belief that its second syllable represents " dynas," a settlement or stronghold. It seems unlikely therefore that

London began as a Roman town, after the conquest of Britain by Claudius, since, in that case, it would have been given a Roman name. The question, too, of the lake or marsh may not be disposed of, even if we grant that the land level was higher in early days than it now is. There must have been marshes near London for the disaster which we shall have to record under Claudius to have occurred, and I notice that Gordon Home, who rejects the hitherto accepted belief that the environs of London were marshy, says that the retreat of Suetonius Paulinus from London, by a route north of the Thames, would have meant that "on the south lay the marsh bordered Thames." This can only mean that, in spite of the higher level of the ground at that time, he still believes the north shore of the Thames to have been marshy.*

When Cymbeline died, somewhere about A.D. 40, his kingdom went to pieces ; his sons quarrelled with one another, and, no doubt, the foreign merchants lacked the protection and encouragement to which they had become acustomed. It was the same story that had to be told again when Ethelbert and Charlemagne died, for in each case the kingdom was the work of the man, and was held together only by him. The Roman Emperor Claudius, who, in spite of his failings, was an able man, saw that the time was ripe for adding Britain to the Roman Empire, and struck

*Roman London, p. 79.

quickly and surely. He sent Aulus Plautius, an experienced and popular general, with four legions and their full complement of auxilliary troops, into Britain in A.D.43; and, since these soldiers were to form an army of occupation, and not merely a raiding force, as those under Cæsar had done, their nationality concerns the British, and indirectly, the London population a good deal.

Three of these four legions, the second (Augusta), the fourteenth (Gemina Martia), and the twentieth (Valeria Victrix) came from the Rhine Army, and were recruited in Northern Gaul. Thus they were very largely of Nordic blood ; indeed there could have been little difference between their ancestry and that of the Southern Britons. The fourth legion, on the other hand, was the ninth (Hispana), from the army of the Danube, a legion recruited in Pannonia and included because it was the old legion of Aulus Plautius, who most likely had asked specially for it. Pannonia lay to the North of the Adriatic, in what is now Jugo-Slavia, and its people were Illyrians and therefore Slavs. From this it would seem that an infusion of the round headed Slav element was introduced into Britain to the extent of some ten thousand men. This may not seem a large number, and indeed the unlucky legion was wiped out by Boudicca twenty years later; still, in twenty years, ten thousand men may have left a distinct impression on the physical anthropology of the district in which they were stationed, and in evidence of this, the record may be quoted of a puzzling light colouration, which was noticed not long ago, in the inhabitants of a certain region in Egypt. Later on this was explained by the fact that formerly a Highland regiment had been quartered there.

Since the Hispana legion was stationed at Ratae (Leicester), and afterwards at Lindum (Lincoln), probably it influenced the London population very little, except that it was kept up to strength, and later on entirely reconstructed from drafts, presumably brought from its recruiting area in Pannonia. These may have passed through and rested in London for some time.

Where Plautius landed is uncertain. Some think at Richborough, others, near Hayling Island; but, in any case, he was opposed by the two sons of Cymbeline, Caradawg or Caratacus and Togidumnus. They were not able, however, to prevent him from pushing on to a town on the Thames which is not named, but possessed a bridge; and this town all authorities seem to agree must have been London. Gordon Home suggests that this bridge had originally been built by Julius Cæsar. Of course it may have been, though we must remember that Cæsar does not mention London, but does mention that he was in a great hurry to leave Britain. Waiting to build a bridge would hardly have helped him, since the ford at Westminster was so close, and now was quite at his disposal. Facts weigh so differently to different thinkers, and in this case they suggest to me that the bridge and the town, which we are told held many merchants, was the work of Cymbeline, whose policy had been to encourage foreign craftsmen, even if his own people had not been capable of bridging the Thames.

It would be very interesting to know what sort of town Plautius found at London, and what inhabitants it contained. That the bridge head was near the southern slopes of Cornhill seems probable enough, for no better site than this for London Bridge has ever been discovered. It is likely, too, from remains which have been found, that something in the way of quays or wharves were attempted along the banks, as well as in the mouth of Walbrook, for British and foreign ships are suggested by the presence of merchants. Even in Cæsar's time the British and Gallic ships are known to have been roomy and solidly built, though in his time they were chiefly confined to Dover and the other harbours on the South and East coast. Most of the dwellings were wattle and daub huts, but the plentiful supply of brick earth most likely was beginning to be used for brick making, and one may imagine, reasonably enough, that some of the wealthier merchants were building villas with hypocausts and brick and timber walls, such as those to which they were accustomed on the continent.

Ptolemy, who wrote his work on Geography about A.D. 140, places London in Kent. It is quite possible that when the bridge was built the earliest inhabitants settled on the southern side ; in which case Southwark is older than London, just as Kingswear in Devon is older than Dartmouth. The advantage of the northern site, however, was so great that it was bound to become very quickly the more important settlement. In any case Ptolemy's description is so sketchy and inaccurate that he may easily have made a mistake as to the shore upon which London stood.

There is every reason to believe that London was becoming a cosmopolitan city, and that artisans as well as merchants were settling there, and beginning to ply their trades ; for a great deal of money had been minted and some must have found its way into the pockets, if they had them, of the craftsmen. How much of the unskilled labour was the work of slaves we do not know ; but probably a good deal.

Among the foreign population Gauls were undoubtedly in excess, and most of these were of the same blood as the Britons, but a certain number of Roman traders almost certainly had pushed ahead of the flag. Among these must have been not only Italians, but members of other Mediterranean nations. Undoubtedly the main population was British, and many of the skulls recovered from the Thames mud in dredging, belonged to them. Unfortunately, however, we have little skill as yet by which we may tell how long a skull has been submerged, and, since the Britons were a nationality containing Nordic, Alpine and

Mediterranean components, it is almost impossible for craniologists to be at all dogmatic about any one particular skull. We can detect the prevalence of the traits of the three great European stocks, but since most European nations are composed of all three of these, it is only occasionally that we can ascribe any particular skull to its proper nationality.

It is something, however, to have learnt our limitations, and we do know that those of us who have had the necessary experience and training can, in many cases, though not in all, give a reliable opinion on the age and sex of a skull, as well as of the stock which preponderates. The practical outcome of this explanation is that antiquaries should submit any skulls or bones which they may find to more than one anatomist, and should ask each for a written report, without telling him any details of the circumstances under which the remains were discovered.

Anyone reading the foregoing will understand that I am not prepared to place any weight at all upon Gordon Home's statement that, at Chelsea, skulls of two different types were found, and that these belonged to Romans and Britons. It is true that he uses it only as one link in a chain of evidence that Cæsar crossed the river at that place ; and it is also true that a chain of evidence is not of the strength of its weakest link. It may well be, as he says, that two types are found, but it does not follow that the one was Roman and the other

British. We must remember that many of the Roman patricians were largely of Nordic ancestry, as also were the British chieftains ; while most of the Roman legionaries were recruited in Gaul, and were perhaps closely related to the Cymric Britons, who had come over here only from fifty to a hundred years before. On both sides, too, was a certain infusion of Mediterranean blood ; on the Roman side derived from plebeian Italian or Mediterranean legionaries, and on the British side from the Long Barrow stock, which, as his colour index, and psychology shows, is still widely present in the Welshman of to-day.

From this digression we return to Aulus Plautius and his legions, who evidently had lost a great many men in their contest with the Britons, and were encamped somewhere near, though probably not within, London. Some people suggest the great camp at Keston, already referred to in connection with Cæsar, as his resting place, though this camp certainly is not a typical piece of Roman work, and it seems unlikely that Plautius, having fought his way across the Thames, should withdraw so far South once more.

Claudius now was sent for, and came with reinforcements, including elephants; joining his general near London, and an advance upon Camulodunum was made, no doubt because it was the seat of the royal house, and the titular capital of South Britain. Caradawg was defeated somewhere between the two towns, probably on the Lea or the

Chelmer, since the Britons seem always to have made a stand on the bank of a river ; and Claudius entered Camulodunum. This, I think, was a very epoch making event from an historical point of view, since it marks the beginning of the Roman occupation of Britain.

As he is said to have spent only sixteen days in Britain, and must have taken ten days at least in leading his elephants from Richborough to Camulodunum, Claudius had little time to give to arranging the future government of the Island ; but Camulodunum remained the capital in spite of the striking advantage of London. Having made an impressive entry into the country, which, from a political standpoint, was quite a wise thing to do, he left the details of its government to Aulus Plautius, and doubtless hurried back to Rome as quickly as he might ; possibly, as Gordon Home suggests, taking ship from Colchester, and leaving his army to follow.

Plautius spread his four legions out in different directions ; the second, under Vespasian, accompanied by his son Titus, subduing the South-West, and establishing itself at Isca Silurum (Caerleon) ; the twentieth remaining at Camulodunum ; the ninth advancing to Ratae (Leicester) ; while the fourteenth, Oman suggests, was most likely stationed where the Fosseway is crossed by Watling Street, possibly at Lactodurum (Towcester). From our point of view the effect was that London automatically became the central point for connecting these legions with the Continent, and the brain of the whole civil and military system of Roman Britain. Camulodunum clearly was impossible as a capital, and the legion holding it was soon freed by making the town a colony for time-expired soldiers.

In A.D. 47 Plautius returned to Rome, and was succeeded by Ostorius Scapula, who, after a few years, was replaced by Suetonius Paulinus. At this time London must have been the depot for the troops at the front, and a continual stream of drafts and time-expired men must have passed through it, though many of the latter, as has been seen, settled in Britain and married British wives. As an instance of this a monument exists, raised by Solinus to his wife Grata, daughter of Dagobitus, which Reginald Smith thinks is a Celtic name, though Gordon Home suggests that it belonged to a Frank named Dagobert.

It would be interesting to know the proportion of Roman women who accompanied the troops over here. In estimating this, one must bear in mind the long marches which the soldiers had to make from the recruiting areas of the legions to their point of embarkation for Britain, as well as the comparatively small size of the vessels which bore them across. It often is said that Roman life in Britain was very like that of our own people in India, and so indeed it was, in that most Roman officials hoped to return to Rome when their working days were over ; but I fancy that only the richest

and most highly placed could afford the luxury of
bringing their wives and families to this country.
It is this consideration which makes me hope that
a specialized study of female Romano-British
skeletons may throw some light upon the physical
characters of the Britons. Another point in
which the anatomist can help the historian, is his
capacity nowadays for sexing skulls and bones
with a rather more than moderate degree of
accuracy ; for where collections, such as those at
Hythe and Rothwell, show a high proportion of
women's and children's bones, they are not likely
to be the result of a battle, however loudly popular
report asserts that they are.

It is likely that the citizens of London at this
stage were beginning to show an increase of
Alpine traits ; an increase tending to become
more marked as time went on. If the busts and
profiles of the Roman Emperors were characteristic of the Roman patricians, there was a great
deal of brachycephaly among them : Julius Cæsar,
for instance, combines Nordic features with a
short broad head, while the stocky solid frame and
bull neck of many of the later imperial portraits
were derived neither from Nordic nor Mediterranean ancestors, but remind us strongly of the
round-headed Etruscan Race from which Peake
has derived his " Prospectors."

When the Romans first occupied London they
gave it no civic rank, and this may frankly be con-
ceded as a point to those who hold that no city

or town existed before this date. Verulam, on the other hand, was given the high rank of a municipium ; while four other towns, Camulodunum (Colchester) ; Lindum (Lincoln) ; Glevum (Gloucester) ; and Eboracum (York) ; were classed as coloniæ. Here I am quoting from Haverfield, who defines the terms more carefully than any one else, and points out that a colonia was a town in which time-expired veterans were planted. It is difficult to be sure which was the more honourable title, though the fact that Camulodunum and Eboracum, each, in its turn, the titular capital of Britain, were coloniæ shows that, if this were an inferior dignity to municipium, it could have been only very little inferior. It seems to me likely enough that London was given no rank at first because it was a suburb or port of Verulam, just as Ostia was, of Rome.

It was during the governorship of Ostorius Scapula and Suetonius Paulinus, that is between A.D. 54 and 61, that the Romans turned the financial screw upon the Britons, and taxed the country to its uttermost capacity. Claudius, who took a kindly interest in the people, made grants of money to help in their development, but when he died, in A.D. 54, and Nero came to the throne, the latter called in every loan which his stepfather had made ; and, at the same time, his old tutor Seneca, the usurious philosopher, demanded the repayment of very large sums which he had placed at interest in Britain.

The blow fell most heavily upon the Iceni of Norfolk, whose late king, Prasutagus, had left half his great fortune to Nero, and the other half to his daughters. The story of the way in which the Roman tax collectors, or tax farmers, seized the whole of this fortune, and outraged the widow Boudicca (Boadicea) and her daughters when they protested, is well known, and probably only a little more infamous than their behaviour elsewhere in Britain. This time, however, they went too far, for the Iceni, and Trinobantes rose and exterminated the whole colony of Camulodunum and, let us hope, most of the tax collectors in it. Horrible details of cruelty which the Britons practised upon the captured Roman colonists, and especially upon their women, are given by Tacitus ; and these are used as instances of the savagery of the two tribes at this period.

It must be remembered, however, that their provocation had been very great, and after the sufferings of their own princesses, their retaliation upon the Roman women may be understood if it cannot be forgiven. On hearing of the outbreak the unlucky ninth legion hurried south from Lindum, but was wiped out by the infuriated followers of Boudicca, who then advanced upon London and Verulam.

Suetonius, the Governor, was at this time in Anglesea, but hastened to London, almost certainly along Watling Street (for by what other road could he have come ?) though this still was

EXPLANATION OF FIG. 21.   Starting from Venta Icenorum
(Caister near Norwich) the forces of Boudicca probably followed
the line marked . . . . . . to Camulodunum, which they sacked.
Here they turned aside to meet and destroy the Ninth Legion,
which had come from Lindum, and for which the nearest route
would have been through Castor on the Nene, and the site which
Cambridge now occupies (assuming that the later Roman roads
were made on the lines of older British trackways).   Its route is
marked thus – – – – – –

After destroying Camulodunum and the Ninth Legion, Boudicca
marched upon London, probably using the trackway which has
been associated with Cymbeline and, later on, was to become the
Vicinal Way.

The route of Suetonius with his cavalry, along the track which
was to become Watling Street, is marked thus – – – – – .   Having
gained London and finding it untenable, he retired on Verulamium
again along Watling Street, followed by Boudicca after she had
wreaked her vengeance upon London (. . . . .).

Boudicca probably reached and destroyed Verulam soon after
Suetonius had left it, but this gave him time to meet the advancing
Fourteenth and Twentieth Legions (° ° ° ° ° °) which he would have
been quite likely to do in the neighbourhood of the Chilterns, and
to choose some defile in the hills in which to make his memorable
stand and to defeat Boudicca.

only the Irish way of the Britons. Haverfield thinks that he came with a cavalry escort ahead of the fourteenth and twentieth legions, and indeed it is difficult to see how he managed to reach London before Boudicca unless this had been the case. Gordon Home suggests that, seeing the impossibility of holding London, he retired with as many of the inhabitants as would accompany him, in a westerly direction, south of the Thames, since to have used even the trackway which crossed the river at Staines, would have exposed his flank to the rebels coming from Verulam. In order to harmonize these two suggestions, both of which seem reasonable enough, we must imagine that uetonius was able, by means of his cavalry scouts, to get into touch with the fourteenth legion advancing along Watling Street ; and to make it cross the Thames, say at Dorchester, to meet him in the country of the Atrebates, and thus to avoid Boudicca, who was on the Watling Street between Verulam and London. On the other hand Oman's suggestion that Suetonius retired from London along Watling Street is possible enough if Boudicca attacked London before Verulam. She would in this case have been travelling south-west from Camulodunum and have entered, sacked, and burnt London soon after he had left it, and, after this, would have followed him along Watling Street to Verulam, treating that town as London had been served. This would have given him time to meet his legions, and to choose a defile in

the Chilterns, near Dunstable perhaps, in which
to make his memorable stand, and to crush the
insurrection. To make this interpretation possible,
however, it is necessary to suppose that Boudicca
took rather longer in covering the fifty miles from
Camulodunum to London than Suetonius had
taken in coming two hundred and fifty miles from
Anglesea. Personally I can see no difficulty in
this, for Tacitus tells us that she had collected
more than 80,000 men, who were accompanied
by thousands of wagons, laden with their wives and
camp followers. Is it unreasonable to think that a
picked cavalry escort, spurred on by the direst
need would have moved five times as fast as a
rabble such as this ?

In any case the Romans under Suetonius
Paulinus were within an ace of losing Britain, and
of having all their work to do again ; even as they
had been, under Julius Cæsar a century before ;
and each time close to Verulam. Their military
skill and determination, however, deserved the
help of Fortune, and on both occasions this
help was forthcoming.

CHAPTER V

LONDON UNDER THE ROMANS

With the defeat of Boudicca the real history of London begins ; for Tacitus, who published his Annals about A.D.116, mentions it by name ; though, unfortunately, he is otherwise very chary of giving the names of places. Before this time our knowledge of London is more or less rational conjecture, gained by piecing together in various combinations what we regard as facts. The discovery of a new fact or the discounting of an old, may make a rearrangement of the whole pattern needful. But when a writer who lived at or near the date of the events which he records, and whose reputation for accurate recording has stood the test of expert criticism, gives us definite statements, these are accepted as history, and there is no room for further conjecture so far as they are concerned. Had Tacitus been a simple recorder of that which he had seen, or gathered from first hand sources, as was Julius Cæsar, we should have learnt much more from him ; but, unfortunately, he was an orator and a stylist before he was a historian, and his striving after effect has resulted in the loss of a great many prosaic details, which we would now give much to know.

In an interesting paper by F. Lambert, in *Archæologia* (The chief publication of the Society of Antiquaries) for 1920-21, a record is given of the discovery of the remains of an extensive fire, from ten to thirteen feet below the modern level, in Nicholas Lane, King William Street and East-cheap. In these were found burnt wood, glass, and Samian ware, burnt coins of Claudius, and burnt clay with the imprint of wattles, against which it had been pressed. This looks suspiciously like the work of Boudicca ; the burnt coins dating the occurrence to a certain extent, and the burnt clay suggesting a collection of wattle and daub huts on the southern slope of Cornhill, between Gracechurch Street, and the Walbrook.

In 1786, wood ashes were found at a depth of 16 feet in Lombard Street,* among which was a gold coin of Galba, who succeeded Nero in A.D. 68. Unfortunately it is not stated whether the coin was burnt, since otherwise it might have been dropped among the exposed ashes at a later date ; and in any case the two discoveries of wood ash need not have been part of the same conflagration. This discovery of what in all probability was Boudicca's revenge, bears out the evidence gained from the position of burials in London. These were not allowed in a Roman town, but usually were situated along the sides of the roads leaving

Archæologia, Vol. 71, p. 57.

it. With one exception no Roman burials are found within an area which Reginald Smith has defined by Cornhill on the North, Thames Street on the South, Walbrook on the West, and Rood Lane and St. Mary at Hill on the East.

This then we must believe was the site of the earliest London, with its wattle and daub huts, such as the Britons used, though it is quite possible that the foreign merchants had well built houses and beautiful gardens upon the twin hill of Ludgate. The question is—was this the remains of an ancient city going back to early British days, as the mediæval Welsh writers would have us believe ?—Was it so new that it owed its origin to the Romans, who had only held the country for eighteen years ; or was it established in the early half of the first century, while Cymbeline was doing all in his power to attract foreign merchants and craftsmen to this land ? To my mind the last suggestion seems to fit in best with the facts we have ; though London's origin must still remain an unsolved problem until fresh facts come to light.

No doubt the result of Boudicca's revolt, which so nearly meant the loss of Britain to Rome, made the Romans resolve that the same thing should not happen again. The Iceni were frightfully punished, and thousands of them must have perished by the sword and by famine : but this was only a beginning. Milder governors than Suetonius were sent, who adjusted taxation and did their best to

Romanize the Southern Britons, and encourage those of them who were law abiding. It would seem to us, looking at things from so far away, that this would have been the very time in which to wall the more important towns, and Dr. Laver, who has studied the archæology of Colchester for a great many years, thinks that the walls of Camulodunum were built soon after Boudicca's rebellion. London, however, is not believed to have been walled until the third or fourth century, and then, apparently, in a great hurry. Perhaps the Romans thought that, as London had now become their base town, and actually, if not nominally, their seat of government, it was more important to ensure that troops should reach it speedily, than that walls should be built which would be of little use without a garrison to defend them. Whether this were the case or not, it was at this time that they began that wonderful road system which was the only lasting heritage they left to Britain except a few London customs.

It seems that they took the existing British chariot roads, many of which had radiated from London, or near it, since Cymbeline's time ; perhaps long before, as the foundation of their system. Indeed, they hardly could have done otherwise, for primitive people have a wonderful sense of direction, and so far as that went, a certain amount of straightening was all that was needed. The real improvement which they undertook was that of making the roads nearly as well

as we make them to-day, and of joining them, one to the other, by other roads where these were wanted.

The forerunner of Watling Street,* the *Sarn Gwyddelin,* or Irish Way of the Welsh historians, has already been spoken of many times as a probable Neolithic trackway from the Kentish coast to Anglesea ; while Ermine Street, which ran North to Lindum, and Stane Street, passing South through the Dorking gap to Chichester (Regnum), formed one continuous artery which may have been part of the road system of Cymbeline, though it does not seem so needful to him as the road from Camulodunum, through London, to Calleva (Silchester), and Venta Belgarum (Winchester), because this latter road joined the capitals of the Trinobantes, the Atrebates and the Belgae, over whom he ruled and between whose capitals he must often have needed to pass.

It will be seen therefore that of the three lines of communication intersecting at or near London, and thus forming six radiating arms, four at least were essential to a king living at Camulodunum, and ruling over the South of Britain. The four essential roads (see Fig. 22) were (1) that from Camulodunum to London, afterwards to become the Vicinal Way ; (2) its continuation through

*The derivation of Watling Street is very uncertain. Some regard it as a corruption of Ætheling, but Windle points out (*The Romans in Britain,* p. 85) that the Watlings seem to have been Scandinavian patrons of handicraft. Since there were two other, much smaller, Watling Streets in England it seems that the name of Ætheling or nobleman's road is not a very likely explanation.

Brentford and Staines to Silchester, the capital of
the Atrebates ; (3 & 4) the two limbs of Watling
Street, which probably had first determined the
site of London, and kept Cymbeline in touch with
the Continent, and London in touch with Verulam.
It is difficult to think of a king ruling over at least
six large tribes in the South of Britain without
these four roads ; and quite as difficult to see how
the place at which they crossed could avoid
becoming an important town, especially since the
roads here also crossed the waterway of the
Thames

The two roads which a king living at Colchester
might have done without, though surely he would
have found them very useful, are (5) Ermine
Street, going to the North, and (6) the Sussex
Stane Street, continuing it to the South coast.

Dr. Laver tells me that he believes the road
leading from Colchester to London to be later than
(7) that passing between Colchester and St.
Albans (Verulam), a large part of which is the
present Stane Street of Essex ; and I can agree
with him fully for the following reasons. When
the Catuvellauni under Tasciovanus conquered
the Trinobantes they first must have subdued the
important border fortress or camp which now is
called Wallbury, at Great Hallingbury, close to
Bishop's Stortford; a camp with a double rampart,
having the river Stort as an extra protection on the
side facing the Catuvellauni. From Bishop's
Stortford to Colchester, Stane Street has a very

straight course through Braintree and Dunmow, and the four places were probably connected by a track, from the time of the earliest settlement of the Trinobantes in the country. When Tasciovanus placed his son Cymbeline upon the throne of the latter people, a communication between his own capital at Verulam and the Trinobantian capital at Camulodunum was a necessity which was reached by joining Bishop's Stortford to Verulam. This part of the track was not paved by the Romans or, if so, it has disappeared ; for the country in the neighbourhood of Much and Little Hadow is difficult, and the modern road has sought easier gradients. At Braintree there are the remains of another British camp, and thus the journey of between fifty and sixty miles, between Verulam and Camulodunum, might be broken, and relays of horses obtained, at two points.

The southern road, from Camulodunum to London, leaves the Verulam road at a place called Mark's Tey, about five miles from the former town, and comes off at an angle ; which means that for five miles after leaving Camulodunum the traveller headed straight for Bishop's Stortford, and then turned to the left, at an obtuse angle, toward London. The fact that the first five miles of the way were laid in the direction of Bishop's Stortford, and not of London, seems a strong argument that the London road was made secondarily, and that five miles of trackmaking

were saved by using the existing Camulodunum
Verulam road. It is needful to the argument to
add that the London road, or Vicinal way, is
recognized as a Roman road, and is not of modern
date ; and it is interesting to notice that, close to
Colchester, the road is still known as Stanway,
which has the same meaning as Stangate at Lambeth, where Watling Street had a paved causeway
between Upper and Lower Marsh. This con-
vergence of highways upon London, only equalled
by that at Corinium (Cirencester), the capital of
the Dobuni, must have added to the mixed
character of London's population ; though a
century or more probably passed before all these
roads were completed.

For two centuries after Boudicca's insurrection
London enjoyed peace, and during this time its
growth and development were rapid. Who can
doubt that many noble public buildings grew up ;
for bricks were made easily enough, and stone
could be brought by river from the Ragstone
Range in Kent. Large buildings were absolutely
necessary in a City from which all the strings were
pulled, and in which all arrangements were made
for the government of the country, as well as for
the upkeep of the legions operating in Wales,
Yorkshire and Scotland. Realizing this, we may
hardly be surprised at the size of the foundations
of the Pretorium, so lately discovered on Cornhill,
nor of the Basilica adjoining it ; though the
foundations of the latter have been known for

some time. The slave market alone must have been an important place, and certainly to an anthropologist it would have been a most interesting one.

The municipal and imperial buildings, however, were probably of less importance than those devoted to religion, if we are to judge by a study of other towns, It is difficult to picture an important town of the Roman Empire without a temple of Jupiter in a commanding position. Unfortunately no remains of any temples can be identified, unless some very firm foundations, found with an altar to Diana, in Foster Lane, Cheapside, may be regarded as such.

Side by side with the Roman deities the Britons worshipped their own gods ; for part of a statue of the *deae matres* has been discovered, and it is possible that the name of Ludgate may still tell the tale of the worship of Lud, who is sometimes confused with Nodens. It has been suggested, too, that Billingsgate recalls, in the same way, the worship of the British god Belinus ; but, until some better reason is given than a superficial likeness in the sound of the two names, it is hard to give Belinus precedence over the Saxon Billings who left their name in so many parts of England. It is probable that Druidism never had much power in London, for Claudius disliked it on account of its cruelties, and though few Roman rulers were so kindly as he, they had every reason to distrust the political leanings of the cult, and the influence which the Druids wielded over the populace. A jug has been found with the inscription " *Londini ad fanum Isidis* " upon it, which certainly suggests that a temple of Isis existed here*; while Mithras was probably as popular among those who had been, or still were, in touch with the army, as he was elsewhere at this time.

Early records of Christianity in London are very scanty. The religion appealed most strongly to the poor and oppressed, and may have gathered quite a large body of believers, without leaving many outward signs. The first adherents, were probably merchants or seamen, in the latter part of the second century ; and, since the British Christians seldom if ever interfered with Roman rule, they got little advertisement in the shape of persecution. Only one Christian Martyr is known to have suffered in London during Roman times, a bishop named Augulus, of whom little is known save that his death was recorded at a time when London was called Augusta, that is after A.D. 340.

Prosperous times make poor history, but there can be no doubt that London became more and more Romanized, and more and more the trading and administrative centre of the country, thereby overshadowing Verulam, and reducing it to the rank of a pleasant country town. We know that the Londoners eagerly copied the Roman dress

---

*Could this refer to Isis, the stream, rather than to Isis the Egptian goddess ?

and manners, and made Latin their speech. Not a single British inscription has come down to us, although there are some in Greek, and many in Latin. One must needs recall, because it suggests so much, the oft quoted legend, found on a brick in Warwick Lane, and probably written during this time. " Austalis dibus XIII vagatur sib cotidim." A free translation of which is—" Austalis goes off on his own every day for a fortnight," and the suggestion is that some workman or slave wrote it about one of his fellows, using Latin in friendly, or unfriendly banter, and writing, it will be noticed, in the present tense when referring to the past, just as a London workman now would be so likely to do.

The acquiescent, even eager way in which the Britons of London received the Romans and made them their models, is a point of some psychological interest when it is contrasted with the fact that, even to-day, the Britons in Wales retain their own speech and ill-suppressed hatred for the Saxon. May not the reason be that Roman influence was present in London from the earliest times, and that no ancient traditions of former independence were severed ? This does not mean that London was necessarily founded by the Romans after the conquest of Claudius, but rather that it grew up as a trading town in the pre-Claudian days, under a British king with Roman leanings ; and that the Romans, treated as welcome guests, behaved themselves as such, and that later on, they never abused the Catuvellaunian Britons of London as they did the Iceni and their Queen Boudicca.

Whether there was an amphitheatre with gladiatorial combats in London is not known. No definite signs of any such place have been brought to light hitherto, although the tombstone of a Greek gladiator was discovered in Tottenham Court Road. This is, of course, no proof that the man actually practised his calling in London, but only that he died there. More convincing signs that there must have been some place for gladiatorial displays are revealed in a dagger and trident which were found in Southwark, and in two or three small figures of gladiators, carved in bone, which are to be seen in the British Museum. It would be strange indeed if a town of London's importance had no amphitheatre, and Southwark, which in so many ways was used as London's playground later on, may well have been its site.

In this golden age of London, between A.D.63 or 64, when Boudicca's ravages had been repaired, and the latter part of the third century, when anxiety was beginning to be felt about Nordic invaders from the other side of the Channel, the city is not mentioned by any author, and all our knowledge is inferential. There is the bronze head of Hadrian, for instance, which was dredged from the river near London Bridge, and seemingly formed part of a very handsome statue, nearly twice the size of life. It suggests that Hadrian was in London when he visited Britain in A.D. 120, bringing with him the sixth legion (Victrix) from the Rhine to replace the unfortunate ninth (Hispana), which suffered so much under Boudicca, and seems to have been wiped out again by the Brigantes of Yorkshire. Contingents of other legions accompanied Hadrian, but since they were all from the Rhine Army, they probably added to the large Celtic element already in the country. Possibly, however, they did more than this, for after Vespasian's day the recruits for a legion were gathered from a different source each year, and in this way Dacians, Spaniards and Moors might, and apparently did, find themselves serving with a nominally Gallic legion in Britain.

It is quite true that few if any of these troops were quartered in London, but they were always passing through, either as recruits, or as invalided and time expired men, and epitaphs tell us that many of them settled and died in the City. From Hadrian's time onward the British garrison began to be recruited locally from Britons, and this practice, at first sight economical, was to lead to a good deal of trouble later on.

Many other suggestions arise as we gaze upon this beautiful head of Hadrian in the centre of the Roman Room at the British Museum, with its keen, clever features, and faint signs of an amused smile waiting its chance to spread over the face. Among them is the thought of how unlikely it is that this was the only statue of its kind, though it is true that only few of the Roman emperors would have made so happy a model.

Now we come to the end of what I have called " London's golden age," and find our own ancestors stirring on the other side of the North Sea ; for about the time when Diocletian became Emperor, in A.D. 284, the Franks, Saxons and Frisians, or Batavians, took to piracy on a large scale and attacked the eastern shores of Britain.   It will be well, I think, to give a little space in order to seek a reason why these Teutonic tribes, which until this time had lived and fought among themselves, as well as with the Roman Empire—but always on land—should have taken so suddenly to the sea. The explanation, the import of which I believe was first grasped by Gibbon, is recorded by Zosimus, who tells us that a band of Franks was removed by the Emperor Probus about A.D. 277 to Pontus, on the southern shores of the Euxine or Black Sea, there to form a barrier against the raids of the Alans.   Hating their exile, they conceived the bold plan of seizing a fleet, and of trying to sail home in it.   In this they succeeded, and coasted through the Ægean and Mediterranean Seas until they reached the rich city of Syracuse, which they surprised and plundered ; then, probably still coasting, for their skill in navigation must have been small, they passed the pillars of Hercules, and the western coasts of Spain and Gaul, until at last they landed, laden with spoils, on the Frisian shore.   Of course, they had great luck, but none deserved it more, and the result of this daring adventure was that the north-west coasts of Europe soon became the nursery of a hardy brood of sea robbers, whose influence upon Britain was to last until to-day.   To me this Frankish Voyage, unknown to ninety-nine Englishmen in every hundred, is one of the earliest, most striking, and most far reaching events in the evolution of the British Empire.

The result of this piracy, for thus I suppose we must regard it, although the occupation was one of the highest honour in those rough and ready times, led to the foundations of the well-known office of *Comes Littoris Saxonici*, and to the appointment of Carausius, a Frisian by birth, to control the British Navy.   Seemingly it was a case of " setting a thief to catch a thief," for he was suspected of keeping the plunder which he recovered from the pirates, and even of having some secret understanding with his old countrymen.   Realizing, therefore, that he was likely to be called to account, he mutinied with his whole navy and induced the Britons to make him their emperor.

His reign of eight years was a wonderful lesson to the Britons of the importance of the command of the sea, had they only been able to understand it, for so long as his ships, manned by Frankish and Frisian mercenaries, held the narrow seas, Rome could do nothing, and the pirates, whom until now Carausius had been keeping in check, found a

fitting vent for their energies in enlisting in this
the first organized appearance of the British Navy.

Of course this state of things must have been
very bad for trade, which would mean hard times
in London. Possibly the interference with the
supply of British grain to the Continent may have
done a good deal to induce the joint Emperors,
Diocletian and Maximian, to recognize Carausius
as their colleague ; a proceeding which the latter
advertised by striking coins in London with his
own and the other two Emperors' heads upon
them.

Soon after this, Carausius, who upon his coins
looks a very brainless, but evidently was a very
capable and daring admiral, was murdered by one
of his lieutenants, named Allectus. This man,
who, by the thickness of his neck, seems to have
had a good deal of Alpine blood in his veins, had
neither the shrewd judgment nor the seafaring
skill of his predecessor, and very soon got into
trouble. For three years Constantius Chlorus had
been building a great fleet in the northern ports
of Gaul, and, in A.D. 296, sailed for Britain. His
own division passed up the Channel to the Thames ;
but another, commanded by Asclepiodotus, slipped
past the fleet of Allectus in a fog, and gained a
landing to the west of the Isle of Wight, whence
he and his force advanced upon London. Allectus,
finding himself outwitted at sea, hurried to protect
London, accompanied apparently by the crews of
his ships, as well perhaps as by other Frankish

mercenary troops held in reserve on shore ; and in the battle which, it seems, took place at Woolmer Forest, close to the borders of Surrey, Sussex and Hampshire, he was defeated and killed.

Luckily Constantius, with his fleet, reached London in time to stay the routed Franks who were busy sacking it, and thousands of them were killed in the narrow streets of the city. It is said by Eumenius that the slaughtered Franks were recognized easily by their long red hair and barbarous dress, and this is a point of some little anthropological interest. More than ten per cent. of red haired individuals is a very rare thing in any race nowadays, and is never reached in the British Isles ; not even in the Central Highlands, where nine per cent. is the highest average noted. The fact that the informants of Eumenius were struck by the prevalence of this colour in the Franks, is worth noticing, therefore. Elton, however, in his *Origins of English History*, gives some quotations from Sidonius Apollinaris which throw another light upon the matter, and suggest that the Franks, at this time, were in the habit of dyeing their hair red ; an explanation which, to the anthropologist, seems much more satisfactory. This is only one instance in history of an oft recurring fashion ; for red hair seems at some periods to have been highly esteemed, and therefore imitated, and at others to have been regarded with great dislike. That it was very common in the Proto-Nordic tribes, and especially among the

Celts, seems certain and it appears also to have often been found among the Danes and Norsemen.

To the physical anthropologist this particular hair colour is interesting because it is so often associated with vitality and restless energy. In the days of mediæval Christianity it was disliked, partly because of the tradition that Judas Iscariot had red hair, and partly, no doubt, because it was so common among the Jews, who in those days were very unpopular.

It seems likely that the galley which was found in digging the foundations of the County Hall at Westminster, and is now in the London Museum, formed part of the fleet of Allectus, sunk by Constantius, since coins of Carausius were found with it. Apparently a hole had been knocked in the bottom of it by a heavy missile, possibly shot from a catapult on the Westminster side, which may have necessitated the beaching of the boat on the Lambeth shore, in order that the crew might escape. A year ago I was asked to examine two skulls which had been found in digging the new foundations of the same building, and at the same depth as that at which the boat had been found. They were both of the male sex, and had gained the characteristic dark brown colour which all skulls recovered from the Thames mud acquire after many years. One was a narrow, and the other a broad skull, and the County Council authorities naturally thought that possibly they might have belonged to two of the galley's crew.   On going into the question, I found that the river mud is liable to "scouring" from time to time, and that, sooner or later, any heavy objects sinking into it will reach the surface of the gravel, where these were found.   Unfortunately there was nothing about the skulls which enabled me to date them, and I was only able to agree that, though they might quite well have belonged to sailors of Allectus, they might equally well have been those of mediæval boatmen.

It is just possible that Allectus may have used part of his three years on the throne in building the walls of London.   Evidently he had small reason to trust the loyalty of the legions, which by this time were recruited largely from Romano-Britons ; and thus he may have thought that a walled city, containing his mint, and for which his fleet could furnish a garrison, would have been a wise insurance in case of a military outbreak.   Unfortunately the only clue to the date of the walls of London, upon which the experts are agreed, is that they were built in a hurry, but the state of things in the time of Allectus hardly seems to justify such haste ; and there was still less cause for it in the time of Carausius.

After this disturbing interlude London settled down to another period of prosperity under Constantius and his son Constantine the Great ; a period which was hardly interfered with by the tyrannical edict of Diocletian against Christians in A.D. 303. Fortunately for the British Christians,

Constantius was a humane man who had a personal liking and respect for those who professed the Faith ;* while Constantine not only reversed the edict of Diocletian, but himself became a Christian on his death bed.   It has already been stated that only one Christian martyr is authentically recorded as having suffered in Roman London, Augulus, Bishop of Augusta, but since London was not called Augusta until after A.D. 336, and Constantine stopped religious persecution in 312, it is difficult to see why this bishop should have suffered.   Perhaps really he was martyred during the time of Constantius, soon after 303, in which year St. Alban of Verulam is believed to have been killed, and some later recorder may have substituted the title of Bishop of Augusta for Bishop of London.   That Christianity was established firmly by A.D. 313 is shown by the fact that Restitutus bishop of London, was present with two other British prelates, at the Council of Arles, summoned by Constantine in that year.   It is thought likely that St. Etheldreda's Church, near Hatton Garden, marks the site of the earliest ministrations of this bishop.

---

*He seems to have been led to Chrisianity through Mithraism.   The two religions had many points in common, though the latter was confined to men.

CHAPTER VI

THE PICTS, THE SCOTS AND THE SAXONS

In A.D. 360 the Picts and Scots were causing so much trouble in the North, that the Emperor Julian, Constantine's nephew, sent Lupicinus to London with troops from Moesia and Batavia. Since the latter were withdrawn after a short time, and were only two regiments strong, their advent cannot have affected the population of London to any marked degree. These Moesic troops were Illyrians in origin, and had probably a mixture of Slavic and Nordic ancestors ; but their stay in London was short, since they were needed in the North.

The origin of the Picts has given rise to much discussion. Oman thinks that they were Caledonians under a new name, thus suggesting, I suppose, that they were Goidels, though Caledonians is a noncommital name, and simply means foresters. Guest, in his *Origines Celticae*, says that, like the Scots, they came from Ireland. To the modern anthropologist the chief interest centres in whether racially, they were more Nordic, or more Mediterranean ; and the latter seems the more probable, if the belief that they were small dark people be well founded. Some hold, though the evidence seems slight, that they spoke an agglutinative language like that of the Basques, and if so, it may have been a remnant of the primitive Mediterranean speech ; though, even if it can be shown that their speech was Gaelic or of some other Celtic origin, there is no reason why they should not have picked it up, as did so many of the Mediterranean tribes. The Scots certainly came to Scotland from Ireland and settled in the Highlands, where, we must believe, they formed the ancestors of the tall, fair Highlanders who still speak the Gaelic or Q. Keltic tongue. Acting in harmony with the Picts and Scots, the Saxons once more began their raids ; and a fourth thorn in the sides of the Romano-Britons were the Attacotti, a North British tribe of Brythonic descent, from among whom the Romans had recruited four regiments for the Continent. These Attacotti labour under the suspicion of having been cannibals, and it is said that when they caught a swineherd with his charge they were more likely than not to eat him before attacking his pigs. This charge of cannibalism, however, was very often and very lightly brought against any enemy in the times of which I am writing, and should not be taken too seriously.

This strangely assorted body of allies penetrated as far south as Kent, and caused so much anxiety for the safety of London that Count

Theodosius, a distinguished Spanish general in the Roman army, was sent in A.D. 368 to drive them back.   So serious was the danger to London at this time, that many people believe this to have been the date at which the walls were hurriedly built.   When they were built we do not know, but the fact that these Attacotti were plundering in Kent without attacking London, seems to show that by this time it was a walled city, and well able to defend itself.   Theodosius must have been an able organizer as well as a good soldier, for, when he had cleared the country of enemies, he reconstructed the arrangements for its defence. He does not seem to have done much directly for London, though no doubt that was his head-quarters, except that he reopened the Mint which had been closed since the end of Constantine's reign.   Indirectly, however, there can be little doubt that he staved off the fate which was to overtake the city a hundred years later.   The relief from immediate danger seems to have led to a very unquiet spirit among the legionaries, who set up Magnus Maximus as emperor in opposition to Gratian.

This Maximus was a Spaniard who had been an officer of Theodosius, and, like him, stayed for some time in Augusta while preparing for a continental campaign ; a campaign which was to drain Britain of men and money, and to encourage the renewed attacks of her eagerly watching foes.

The part of the ring of foes which was most

aggressive at this time, was that formed by the
Irish under King Niall, from whom the O'Neals
claim descent. They attacked Wales chiefly ;
but by A.D. 388, when Maximus had been defeated
and put to death by Theodosius the Great, the
Picts and Saxons joined them, and the pressure
must have been even greater than that from which
Count Theodosius, to distinguish him from his son
Theodosius the Great, had delivered the country
twenty years before. This is the time which is so
ably reconstructed, from the historical novelist's
point of view, by Kipling in *Puck of Pook's Hill.*

Gordon Home suggests that this troublous
time would have made the Londoners look to
their defences ; and it is quite likely that the
bastions were now added to the walls, since it
seems pretty clear that they are of later date than
the land wall. It is possible, too, that the river
wall may have been built at this time, as an insurance against a Saxon fleet passing the defence
of the Count of the Saxon shore and sailing up to
Augusta. It may be suggested that, since the
bastions and river wall seem later than the land
wall, this would have been a time when both of
them were needed badly, if already they had not
been built.

The closing years of the fourth century and the
early ones of the fifth, were sad enough for Britain,
and sadder still for Augusta. Honorius, the weak
minded son of the great Theodosius, was now
emperor, but was fortunate enough to have as

his commander-in-chief a Vandal named Stilicho, who met, and for a time defeated, the many waves of invaders pouring into the Empire. Looked at from a European rather than a purely British standpoint, it is quite clear that Britain was feeling only the edge of a mighty flood of North European humanity, which had burst its banks, and poured in all directions over the Roman empire. This inundation is known to historians as the *Migration of the Nations*. Had the northern tribes focussed their attacks upon Britain alone, the danger, no doubt, would have been met by reinforcements sent from Rome, but, since the attacks were made at the same time upon all parts of the empire, including its very heart, and since Britain was only an outlying member, all the legions were withdrawn from it to defend the more vital parts. Thus Honorius had no choice, in A.D. 410, but to tell the Britons that they must defend themselves.

This is often looked upon as an epoch making event, but it seems that too much stress may be laid upon it, for it must be remembered that Britain had long been suffering from attacks of the Saxon sea rovers on her eastern shores, and the edict of Honorius neither increased nor diminished these : they went on just the same. Then, too, there was no formal withdrawal of Romans from Britain : legions and auxilliary forces, largely recruited from Britons, were called away from time to time and never came back, but their places, no doubt, were filled by new formations, altogether made up of Britons or Romano-Britons. No new general or officials were sent from Rome after A.D. 410 ; but this does not say that all the high officials left in a body for Rome.

So far as Augusta is concerned, it is likely enough that most of the officials were Romano-Britons, by which is meant Britons who had assumed the Roman traditions and methods of government, with the language, dress and habits of Rome, but in whom there was very little Italian blood. It even is likely that Augusta and the other walled towns held most of the Britons trained to affairs, since roving bands of Picts, Scots, Saxons and Attacotti must have made the country villas very undesirable places in which to dwell. This is confirmed, as Haverfield points out, by the fact that few coins later than A.D. 375 are found in their ruins. Surely it is a mistake to believe that, when Rome withdrew her protection, Britain collapsed. Nordic peoples do not often collapse when thrown upon their own resources, and Britain, as we have seen, was largely a Nordic country at this time. That the Britons doggedly fought a losing fight against their Saxon foes until the thirteenth century, and are now effecting a peaceful penetration of England at a greater rate than English people are entering Wales, is not, I submit, an unfair epitome of the course of events.

After A.D. 410 there is very little real history to tell what happened in London, and how its inhabitants fared, for very many years ; thus we are

thrown back upon legends which, no doubt, contain truth as well as fiction, though these are very
difficult to part, and upon rational deductions,
based on the remains which we are able to unearth,
as well as on our knowledge of human nature,
which it is said " is always the same." It seems
impossible that there could have been much
foreign trade going on in the city while the
civilised part of the continent was overrun by
barbarians. It seems, too, quite fair to suggest,
as is so often done, that most of the merchants
went away, were it not so difficult to see whither
they could go. Perhaps all the able bodied
young men were sent to fight the Picts and Scots
in the north-western parts of the island, while
the older men attended to the commissariat
and administrative duties, thus anticipating the
conditions with which Londoners were so familiar
during the Great War.

It seems that, for a good many years, the Picts
and Scots gave more trouble than did the Saxons ;
perhaps because the energies of the latter were
being used in other parts of the Roman Empire.
In any case their troubles and dangers did not
prevent the British clergy from taking a great
interest in the free thought of their fellow monk
Pelagius, who doubted the existence of original
sin. A synod accordingly was held in A.D. 429,
which was attended by St. Germanus, bishop of
Auxerre, as well as by Lupus, bishop of Troyes, in
which Pelagianism was branded as a heresy. After

the synod these bishops venerated the shrine of St. Alban at Verulam ; and, because they postponed this act until the synod was over, Gordon Home thinks that the latter was not held in Verulam but in London. Be this as it may, the fact that so much attention was paid to a matter of dogma, and that many of the British magnates appeared in gorgeous apparel at the synod, shows that things could not really have been desperate at this time in Britain, or at least in that part of Britain near London. After his ecclesiastical duties were discharged, the Britons asked Germanus, who was a soldier as well as a saint, to help them in their campaign against the combined Picts and Saxons. This he did so successfully that the " Hallelujah victory " was gained, and the pressure on Britain relieved for a time. It is not known where this victory took place ; nor whether the Saxons left Britain or stayed there.

The doings of Germanus are recorded by Prosper of Aquitaine, who wrote his Chronicle about A.D. 455 and is regarded by historians as a reliable source. His evidence shows that Saxons were invading the country in A.D. 429, but when they began actually to settle we do not know, though it was quite possibly before this time.

Gildas, a monk of the great monastery of Bangor Iscoed on the Dee, who wrote his " Liber Querulus" about A.D. 545, is responsible for most of the story of the landing of Hengist and Horsa in Thanet, in A.D. 447. It will be noticed that he wrote a century after the events which he recorded are said to have happened, and that, from his cell in Bangor, he could not, in that troubled time, have been in touch with those Saxons of East Kent to whom the doings of their ancestors had been handed down for three generations. Unfortunately Gildas was not a careful historian, and gives us few clues by which we may trace the authority for which his statements were made. Had he been accurate as to the events which may be checked from other sources, we might give him credit for having good information, now lost, about the coming of Hengist and Horsa, and the battles at Aylesford and Crayford. Often, however, he was not accurate, even in great matters like the building of the northern walls, and his account of the later days of Roman Britain does not always tally with that of older historians, nor does it bear the light of modern archæological research.

It is easy, however, to be too hard upon Gildas ; it is especially easy for an Englishman to be too hard upon him, for his unrestrained rhetoric, helpless whining and mingling of religion with venom, all give a bad impression to English readers, which should make them all the more careful to do him justice where they may. That his historical statements are often shaky there can be little doubt, but sometimes, though the details will not bear too strong a light, the general picture may give an impression which is true enough. The oft quoted " Groans of the Britons " may have been very

different from the actual message sent to Aetius in
his third consulate, but it gives us a picture, quite
likely to be true, of what the Britons were suffering
at that time.   The mention of Aetius, although
called Agitius, dates the time in which the Britons
were suffering so sorely to the year A.D. 447.   We
must think too that Gildas had it in his mind, not
so much to record events for future use, as to quote
the misfortunes of his countrymen, and the
barbarity of their Saxon conquerors as object
lessons of the results which needs must follow
looseness in morals, and lukewarmness to the
Church of which he was a priest.

Another and a later account of the Saxon invasion, from the British point of view, is the *Historia
Brittonum*, a compilation of legends attributed to
Nennius and put together during the later years of
the seventh century.   In it are to be found most of
the familiar tales which, learnt in our school days,
made Hengist, Horsa, Vortigern, Vortimer and
Rowena such living personalities.   Indeed, some
thirty years ago, I was assured definitely that the
bones under the high altar in Hythe Church were
those of Saxons defeated by Vortimer, the son of
Vortigern ; a tradition which seems to have been
evolved by a former schoolmaster of the town, who
evidently had read extracts from the *Historia Brittonum*.   Nennius certainly had Gildas before him
when he wrote, as well as Prosper, the biographer
of St. Germanus, and the *Scripta Scotorum Anglo-
rumque*, about which I wish that I knew more.

Probably he had other legends and traditions, now lost, but his records, which include some of King Arthur, are certainly still less reliable than those of Gildas.

On the English side is Bede, the scholarly monk of Wearmouth near Jarrow, who gained his knowledge from Gildas and Nennius, as well as from tradition and folklore which he collected from many correspondents. The work for which we are most indebted to him is his *Historia Ecclesiastica Gentis Anglorum*, in which he traces the Angles, Saxons and Jutes from their continental homes to their various settlements in Britain. For his Kentish history, in which, of course, the landing and subsequent work of St. Augustine interested him most, he relied upon the help of Albinus, an Abbot of Canterbury, who lived in the early half of the eighth century, and must have had in his keeping all the records which Canterbury owned. While the numerous pastorals and records from Rome were obtained for him by Nothelm, who then was arch priest of St. Paul's in London, and afterwards became archbishop of Canterbury.

Bede, so far as we know, never went farther from Jarrow than York, and thus all his knowledge was gleaned from the writings and observations of others ; though, in the quiet earnestness with which he sets down the truth as he believes it, his writings are a pleasing contrast to those of Gildas and Nennius. Yet here again we must not judge the historian on his style, however it may appeal to us : the facts are all that matter, and we must remember that Bede wrote his History in A.D. 731, three hundred years after the Saxon invasion.   I often wonder how much we should be able to reconstruct, from tradition, of the history of the years about 1626, if most of our written records had been destroyed.   It must not be thought that Bede's main object was recording secular history, for this was only a side issue with him, and evidently did not interest him nearly so much as the description of miracles, in which he shows a childlike credulity, or the proper time at which to celebrate Easter. That he honestly believed everything he wrote is certain enough, but I cannot think that anyone who has read through the Ecclesiastical History would look upon him as a very discriminating judge of what is likely to be true.

The fourth work which claims to describe the coming of the Saxons is the Anglo-Saxon Chronicle, a West Saxon record, seemingly begun with Alfred's help, and carried on until the death of Stephen. Its early entries largely incorporate Bede's work, though, when they differ, Bede's original descriptions seem to agree .best with modern archæological research.

I cannot help feeling that for many pages London and its people seem to have been quite forgotten ; there is so little recorded about the City in these days that it is necessary to picture as clearly as we may what was happening all round it, in order that we may appreciate and criticise

the suggestions and inferences which have been
made as to its fate.

The only direct reference to London by name
between A.D. 400 or a little later, when the British
section of the *Notitia Dignitatum,* an itinerary
with mileages between the Roman stations, mentions it, and A.D. 601, when Pope Gregory wished
Augustine to take the title of Archbishop of London,
is to the flight of the defeated Britons to Lunden-
byrig from Crecganford in A.D. 457. I suppose
that there can be no doubt that from this latter
name our modern Crayford is derived ; for, although
there has been much building and excavating at
Crayford in late years, and we know that it was the
site of a palæolithic flint factory, no remains of the
4,000 Britons who are said to have been slain, nor
of their arms or ornaments, have come to light.

It is important to realize that all the details of
the coming of the Saxons are legends rather than
records ; that is to say that, though they have
been written at some time or another, we do not
know how long after the date of their happening
they were first set down, nor do we know how many
fanciful additions by ingenious scribes have been
made. For this reason we are seeking with great
care for any scraps of direct evidence which will
strengthen or weaken the hitherto unsupported
testimony of the early writers.

That a very large population of long headed,
clean limbed, Nordic men and women inhabited
the island of Thanet or Ruym, from which the

name of Ramsgate is derived, we know for certain ;
since hardly a year passes but some fresh discoveries of their bones are made. We know too
that they bore arms and wore ornaments exactly
like those found with skeletons of the same build
on the Rhine in the neighbourhood of Cologne ;
we are unable therefore to believe Bede's statement
that these people came straight from Jutland,
though of course they may have done so originally.
Then we find that they had certain burial customs
which were unknown to the Saxons, using that
name in a very general sense, who buried their
dead elsewhere in England, except in the Isle of
Wight and the Meon Valley of Hampshire. We
may, therefore, accept readily enough the statement of Gildas that a number of Nordic pirates
came into Thanet: nor, I think, need we refuse to
believe that their leader was Hengist for the deeds
of a Dane of this name are sung in the early
English poem of *Beowulf*—how he fought with
Finn, the King of Friesland and how the tribe to
to which he belonged was " Eotena " or that of the
Jutes. What became of this Hengist the poem
does not say. It is, however, significant that he
was a contemporary of our Hengist and that he
is last heard of in Friesland, which is no great distance from the site whence some at least of the so-
called Jutish invaders of Thanet must have come.
It is very unlikely that there were two leaders, both
called by the uncommon name of Hengist, carrying
on successful piracy in the Channel at the same

time ; and therefore I can see many reasons for, and none against, believing that the Kentish Hengist was the Hengist of Beowulf, who had raised a war band of Franks and Frisians, and landed in Thanet, with or without the consent of Vortigern, or Guorthigion, to give him his British name. That Hengist was known to be a Jute may explain Bede's belief that all his followers were Jutes too. Those who care to go more fully into the matter, which hardly concerns London, will find it fully discussed by Chadwick (*Origin of the English Nation*) so far as the knowledge of 1906 allows him to go.

The war band, having made good its landing, was followed by great numbers of kinsmen until the little island of Thanet could hold no more ; and, treaty or no treaty, they were bound to cross the Wantsum at Sarre and to spread into Kent. That this would lead to trouble with the Britons who inhabited the fertile land called Caint, north of the great forest of Andred (in Celtic " the uninhabited region ") is natural enough ;· and before long little squabbles would lead to a racial war in which the Britons, following their old tactics, chose a river on which to make their stand. There is nothing therefore to make the battle of Aylesford or Aeglesford, which Guest says means the ford of the church (from the British word *Eglws*, derived from the Greek *Ecclesia*), or that of Crayford improbable : indeed, since both these sites were fords on Watling Street and the Pilgrim's Way, res-

pectively, there is much to support the probability
of these battles having actually happened, except
that no evidence of such, in either place, has yet
been found.

Oman says that " Saxon graves of the pagan
period give us a good deal of information concern-
ing the social life and culture of the incoming race,
but not definite history;" yet, if these graves are
able to tell us, as Thurlow Leeds* has shown, that
these people came from the Middle and Lower
Rhine and not from Jutland, it is surely a little
pedantic to refuse to their testimony the rank of
history.   On the opposite side of the channel were
two great confederacies, a northern one holding
the Angles, Chaucians, Frisians, Warings and
possibly other tribes ; and a southern one which
was mainly Frankish though partly Frisian.   It
looks as though the so called Jutes and Batavians
or Southern Frisians were more closely in touch
with the southern group, and that the dwellers in
East Kent included a large Frankish element ; a
suggestion becoming all the more likely when we
remember that one of the early Kentish kings was
called Hlothere, a name borne by one of Charlemagne's sons.

The origin of these primitive Men of Kent, however, fascinating though it be, only touches London
indirectly ; since they do not seem to have followed
the defeated Britons in their flight from Crayford
to London, but to have retired east of the

* *Archæology of the Anglo-Saxon Settlements.*

Medway, where alone their characteristic grave furniture is found.

According to Gildas, Vortigern was leading the Britons ; and, after his day, his son Vortimer seems to have fought the Kentish invaders many times. Another recorded leader of the Britons in Kent, who clearly was a real personage, was Ambrosius ; and it is fairly certain that all these must have used London as their base, though Gildas says nothing about it. The fact that all the energies of the Britons seem to have been used against their Kentish foes, suggests that, for some considerable time after they came, no fresh landings of other marauders were taking place.

The relations of the settlers of West Kent to the so-called Jutes of East Kent is a very difficult one to clear up : that they were tribes with different burial customs is certain ; and that the Medway divided the two peoples, as indeed it divides still the Kentish Men from the Men of Kent, is just as sure. It has been suggested that the Kentish Men who settled in West Kent were Frisians or Batavians, who were close neighbours of the Franks on the Continent, and seem to have controlled most of the shipping from the mouths of the Rhine. The suggestion, so far as I know, has nothing against it ; it is borne out by the likeness of the Kentish dialect to the Frisian ; and, furthermore, the well known spirit of independence of the Frisians seems to come out in the repeated Kentish risings, when the people thought that they were being unfairly treated. I cannot help thinking that the men who so readily and rashly followed Wat Tyler, Jack Cade and Sir Thomas Wyatt, were of Frisian blood; though I must confess that there are no records, such as are found in Dumfries and Holderness, to support this belief.

It seems likely that Essex, Sussex and Wessex were settled by men of the northern confederacy, who came some time after the arrival of the Jutes, thus giving the Britons time to concentrate all their efforts against the latter people. With the South Saxons London has nothing to do, but with the East and West Saxons the case is different. Little is known as to how or when Essex was settled, though it seems more than likely that many separate landings were made from the numerous creeks and river mouths in the broken coast line, while the Britons were busy with their Kentish assailants.

It is not at all certain that the Saxons called themselves by this name at first, any more than that the survivors of the Britons call themselves Welsh. Probably in each case the term meant stranger or foreigner, and Saxon was the collective name used by the Franks for neighbours of the northern confederacy; especially of the Chaucians, who were living a little to the North of them when Tacitus wrote, but are lost sight of by that name later. To try, as Bede did, to separate the Angles from the Saxons, and to define distinct areas from which each came, seems rather to lead

us off the track than to help us along it, and, understanding this, our present method is to examine
and record carefully the details of every find, in
order that it may be compared with others in this
country, as well as with those on the Continent.

Place names also are being investigated most
thoroughly, and here too there is hope of help. If
we take, for example, the case of the Billings, who
are believed to have been the royal house of the
Warings, we find their name in Billingsgate in
London, Billingborough and Billinghay in Lincs,
Billinge and Billington in Lancs, Billingham in
Durham, Billing in Northants, Billingshurst in
Sussex and possibly Bellingham in Kent; and it
must be remembered that the Warings were so
closely associated with the Angles that the " Leges
Anglorum et Varinorum " are always mentioned
together. Here then is a clan, members of which
found their way into districts belonging, according
to Bede, to the Angles, Saxons and Mercians. If
other clans were broken up in the same way, it is
not surprising that it is difficult to find any
sharply marked cultural differences in the various
geographical regions, except Kent.

The settlement of Wessex is more difficult,
and at the same time more interesting than that of
Essex. The Anglo-Saxon Chronicle tells us that
in A.D. 494 Cerdic and Cynric, his son, landed at
Cerdicesora (Charford ?) from five ships, and
then worked their way North, defeating a British
King named Natanleod in A.D. 508. This Natan-

loed is supposed to have been the famous Romano-British general, Ambrosius Aurelianus, already mentioned, whose praises were sung by Gildas. It is quite possible that this landing was made, though it has been pointed out that Cerdic is a Celtic, rather than, a Saxon name, and is merely Cáràdawg or Caràdoc, which is quite a common name in Wales to-day. To the Romans it was Caratacus; while in Modern England it has become Cradock.

The view which finds most favour with archæologists to-day is that Wessex was settled mainly by bands which passed up the Thames in their longships, and then up the various tributaries of that river, until they came to places which appealed to them as sites for their settlements. Granting this, it casts an important side light on the state of London, by which they were able to pass without trouble; thus showing that the city either could not, or would not, take offensive measures against them; whatever it might be able to do for its defence against direct attack. Thurlow Leeds has shown, in his map of Saxon burial grounds, how closely most of them keep to the smaller tributaries of rivers, but I think that his belief that they were reached altogether by ship is open to some criticism. In the first place many of these streams would not float a ship carrying a number of men with their wives and families; and if the ships were of very light draught, their breadth must have been greater; while the rivers must have been wide enough to take not only the ship, but the oars on each side as well. I can foresee the arguments with which Mr. Leeds would meet this criticism ; but there is yet another reason for opposing his belief. If we look at his map we find the head waters of the Warwickshire Avon thickly fringed with burial grounds. Indeed two new ones, at Bidford and Stratford, have been excavated in the last year or two. Does he want us to agree that the settlers here came round Land's End, up the Severn, and so to the Avon ? Unless he can make us do so, why should we believe that the settlers on other streams reached their final resting places entirely by water ? But, after all, the matter is a small one, and we may agree with him upon the likelihood of the Saxons going as far as they comfortably could in their boats, and then striking across country until they found a dry spot, near a stream, on which they might come to rest.

This question of a dry site was a very important one to the Saxons, who, as Leeds has shown, lived in cots, the floors of which were below the level of the ground ; and anyone through whose hands a large number of their bones has passed, will agree as to their terrible sufferings from chronic rheumatism or osteo-arthritis. A good example is the burial ground lately uncovered by Col. Bidder at Mitcham, on the banks of the Wandle ; the discovery of which was due to the excavation of gravel from a field. The Saxons had noticed this patch of gravel, amidst the London clay, fourteen hundred years ago, and had taken advantage of it. Often in the chalk country they chose the side, generally the south side, of a down in preference to a stream, as at Margate, Folkestone, Dunstable and Purley ; but the point which needs clearing up is how far the burial grounds were from the dwelling places, and whether each one suggests a hamlet in its immediate neighbourhood.

CHAPTER VII

SAXON LONDON

What the attitude of the Saxons was to London is a very difficult question to answer. The likelihood, almost the certainty, of its being used as the headquarters ot the Britons, under Vortigern, Vortimer and Ambrosius, has already been dwelt upon ; but later, when the foe was gradually closing round it, the fighting Britons, must have deserted it even though the non-combatants stayed behind. What became of it between A.D. 500 and 600 is one of the greatest puzzles of history. We are sure that noble buildings were there when the legions left, because we are finding their foundations to-day. On the Continent the ruins of Roman buildings remain, but in London they have all disappeared save the walls. If the great pillars and capitals had been worked into other meaner buildings we should see them still, and it is impossible that they should have been taken away by sea. I cannot help thinking that, when the East Saxons did enter London, they used the stones of the buildings in order to repair their roads ; for I can think of no

other reason which would have made it worth
their while to break up great pillars belonging to
the few capitals which still remain,. into such
small pieces that now they cannot be recognized.

And then after say A.D. 500, when Saxon settlers
were becoming plentiful along the river banks,
could anyone hostile to them have lived in London? If they did, whence did they draw their
supplies ?   The more I think of it the more sure I
feel that there must have been a working agree-
ment about London between the Britons and the
English ; and possibly this was only one of many
such throughout the country, for one of the
psychological characters of the Englishman is
that, though he is pugnacious enough while
actual fighting is going on, he is always ready to
make friends as soon as the fight is over ; or,
indeed, during any interval in the fight.   It is not
impossible that Londoners traded with the Saxons
around them, and supplied them with wine, oil
and such like things in return for food and wool ;
for it is quite clear that had London been of no use
to them, and, still more, had it been a danger to
them, the Saxons would have found no difficulty
in wiping it out by cutting off all supplies ; even if
they had not cared to carry it by assault.

Besant makes a great point of London having
been derelict for generations, utterly abandoned by
the British and ignored by the Saxons ; but
Gomme shows that its customs and laws were
handed down from Roman to mediæval and

modern English days. If we are to point to the law of gavelkind as a sign that the Kentish people had a different origin from the rest of the Saxons, it is difficult to see how we may logically ignore the Roman custom of dividing property into three parts on the owner's death—one for the widow, one for the children and a third to be distributed by will in any way he pleased—a custom which survived in London until the time of George the First.

Gordon Home thinks that London became English about A.D. 570, and that in the battle which Æthelbert of Kent fought with Ceawlin, king of Wessex, at Wibbandun (Wimbledon), the former was defending his lately gained city. This is a new suggestion, and to make it possible the dates need adjusting a little; for the battle, according to the Saxon Chronicle, was fought in A.D. 568, when Æthelbert was only sixteen. In any case Ceawlin was the victor, and if the battle were really in the defence of London, we must presume that the town passed to the West Saxons. The entry in the Chronicle gives me quite a different impression to this, and perhaps it may be as well to quote it. " Anno. DLXVIII. In this year Ceawlin and Cutha, Ceawlin's brother, fought against Æthelbert and drove him into Kent; and slew two aldormen at Wibbandun, Oslaf and Knebba." Reading between the lines of this I should have said that Ceawlin had caught the young Æthelbert trying to extend the Kentish domains by

poaching on what he regarded as West Saxon
territory, and had sent him back into his own
country with a thrashing. Had Ceawlin been
threatening either London or Kent there was
nothing to stop his advance after his victory ;
but, instead of advancing against either, he seems
to have gone off to his great campaign in the West.*
But, although I think that Home's line of
argument is doubtful, I am at one with him in
believing that, early in Æthelbert's reign, London
became a Saxon town ; though it seems that the
East Saxons and not the Kentish men were the
first to take it over ; and this, no doubt, was due
to the fact that it lay on their side of the river, and
therefore within their sphere of influence.   A possible common interest between London and Essex
may have been the slave trade, which had been an
organized industry before Cæsar's day.   In the
endless recorded and unrecorded fights between the
Britons and Saxons, as well as between the already
settled invaders and those who came later, a great
many captives must have been made.   If these
could be taken to London a ready sale was sure
enough, since Chadwick reckons that a slave in
England was worth a pound of silver, but that
on the Continent he would fetch three or four
times as much.

* Again I must quote the valuable Saxon discovery at Mitcham.
The burials here, dated by fairly plentiful grave furniture, are of the
4th and 5th century, and everything points to their being remains of
West Saxons.   At Wimbledon, therefore, Ceawlin seems to have been
in his own country and among his own people, and Æthelbert must be
looked upon as an intruder.

The well known anecdote of Gregory, in the market at Rome, shows that slaves, even from Deira, were on sale there about the year A.D. 585 ; while a little more than a hundred years later the trade had grown so much that Ine of Wessex found it necessary to pass a law forbidding the sale of English slaves out of the country.

Those who believe, and I confess that I am one of them, that London's customs and traditions have been handed down, in part, from Roman times without a break, can only hold that the strength of its walls and the superstitious dread of the invaders enabled a certain number of its inhabitants to live through the earlier years of the conquest ; and that gradually they established a trade with the conquerors who became settlers round them.

Later on, in A.D. 601, Gregory, who now had become Pope, sent a consecrated pallium to Augustine with directions that he should have himself consecrated Archbishop of London ; but it was clear enough to Augustine that the step was impracticable, since London was now in the hands of the East Saxons, who, in their turn, were subject to Kent. Had Gregory understood the position of affairs better, he would have seen that Canterbury, the Bretwalda's capital, could not have been passed over as the Metropolitan see for a town of the East Saxons. The fact, however, that Pope Gregory mentioned London at all, shows that it was to his knowledge a living city at this time, and one of the most important in England. One of our greatest difficulties in understanding this stage of early Saxon London is that we have so little knowledge of the terms upon which the Britons and Saxons lived.

I think that we must recognize in the Saxon temperament, as in that of other Nordic people, a capacity for living two quite separate lives. During the stage of conquest, while the active fighting was going on, the Saxon was little short of a devil, sparing neither age nor sex, and literally intoxicating himself with bloodshed : whether he was to kill or be killed mattered nothing to him so long as blood flowed freely ; indeed he was able to work himself up into a state of homicidal ecstacy, in which probably he could not have felt the stroke which killed him. In this frame of mind he would destroy any man, woman, child or animal which came in his way, and would burn homesteads, cornfields, and, with greater pleasure still, monasteries and their inhabitants. It was at sea, however, that this side of the character of the Old English was shown to the full. They were known and dreaded far and wide for the utterly fearless way in which they chose the worst weather for their raids, since they knew that their victims would then least expect them. Robbers, murderers and ruthless pirates they certainly were ; but in their glorious energy, hardihood and endurance, they were only equalled by their successors and kinsmen the Norsemen and

Danes. This was the dangerous, destructive creature which the British historians knew and painted
for us as a fiend from hell : not that the Briton
was any better, save that the Mediterranean
element in his composition made him less sus-
ceptible to the wild joy of the fight, and more
crafty and cautious in his movements : quite
enough to turn the scale against him in open,
hand to hand fighting.

But when the fighting was over for a time, and
the invader became a settler whose blood had
cooled, the Saxon was a very different person. He
then became a hardworking tiller of the ground,
enjoying the fertile soil and rich pastures which
were so much better than anything he had known
in earlier days. He became law abiding, good to
his wife, whom he treated as a companion instead
of as a drudge, and utterly loyal to his lord.

How striking it is, when we think of the ruthless
savagery of the Saxons and other Nordic Folk at
war, and in their pirate days, that their conversion
to Christianity should have been so easy, and
accompanied by so few martyrdoms, and by so
little persecution of missionaries.

I have tried in earlier pages to lay stress on the
difference between the Nordic and the Mediterranean forms of cruelty : how the Norseman slew
and maimed without thinking or caring how much
pain he gave, while the Mediterranean criticised
and appreciated every detail of the suffering which
he watched and enjoyed. When Christianity came

to the former it found a mentality quite able to understand its gentler teachings, though, until then, the possibility of there being a religion which tried to do good to all mankind had never been grasped. Neither the Romish nor the Irish Church had the least difficulty in obtaining a fair hearing from the Saxons; though, of the two, the Irish Church seems to have appealed to them most successfully.

Those who, like Baldwin Brown,* have studied the handiwork of the Saxons most carefully, assure us that they were by no means the brutal savages that the British historians would have us believe. We know that in their home life there were many among them able to execute refined and beautiful work, and also that the general taste for skilful workmanship and harmonious colour schemes was very good.

When we study their language and literature, we feel that we are dealing with a people whose thoughts went far beyond the humble needs of mere barbarians. Anglo Saxon was anything but a simple and childish tongue, for it abounded in a wealth of words which allowed very delicate shades of expression. It was a language in which all the true spirit of poetry could be brought out, by which the strongest and most telling calls could be made upon all that was good in the minds of its hearers, and that in few words. It is sad to think that at least a fifth of this strong and

* *Arts and Crafts of Mediæval England.*

manly tongue has been lost to us through the mistaken belief of our writers, after the Conquest, that, by using words culled from the French, they were showing knowledge and learning ; when all that they did was to weaken their own speech by allowing the English equivalents of their new words to drop out of use and die.

I have, however, neither the will, nor is it in my power, to judge modern literary English. All that I would say is that when a Saxon wished to make the things of everyday life thoroughly clear, when he wished to touch the hearts of his listeners and to carry them with him ; or even when he wished to discuss abstract ideas, his own home tongue was ready with the very words wanted, and there was no need for him to use many ; though there were many from which he might choose. A people who had built up a language which could serve them so well surely were not barbarians.

For the so called poetry of the Saxons I have no good word to say ; for this, as Sharon Turner long ago pointed out, was a craft of its own, governed by many quaint rules, the object of which was to keep it in the hands of the scop or professional poet. It is true that it seems to have acted as a stimulant to its hearers ; but, since it was usually taken with long draughts of ale and mead, we may suppose that these were necessary for its true appreciation. I cannot think that it is worthy to rank with the straightforward clearness of Saxon prose.

It was a people like this whose hamlets were closing gradually round London in the early and middle parts of the sixth century ; at Mitcham and Croydon, at Sanderstead and Purley, on the South, as we know, and no doubt at places equally near on the East and West. It seems likely enough that they came to a " live and let live " understanding with the Romano-Britons of London, since the fighting Britons must have retired westward by this time. Moreover Romano-British coins are so often found in early Saxon graveyards, that it is difficult to believe that some trading relations did not exist between the two peoples.

We are told by Gildas that even while fighting was going on some of the Britons saved their lives by becoming the slaves of the Saxons, and that their lot was a very hopeless one. So undoubtedly it was at first, but in all ages the treatment given to a slave has depended a good deal upon the value which the owner set upon him or her. When the bitterness of the fighting was over, an intelligent and useful slave could improve his lot to a great extent by tactful and willing behaviour, unless he had the misfortune to fall into the hand of a brutal master who took a pleasure in causing needless suffering. Such a master I do not think that the Englishman in his home life would have made. The question which it is so difficult to settle is whether there are any signs of Britons having been on terms of real friendship with the

Saxons; terms which would allow us to think that sometimes the two people might have intermarried. I cannot think that at this early stage any such thing happened, since the Saxons were very proud of the purity of their race, and hardly ever married outside it. Later on, no doubt, there came a certain mingling of the two peoples, as in the case of Alfred's friend and biographer, Asser, who was a Welshman. Perhaps it is not wise to think too much of the English always as the conquerors and of the Britons always as the conquered, for there were times, like that of the battle of Mount Badon, when the conditions were reversed, and there were long periods too when the two peoples lived side by side, having agreed upon a common boundary.* When this was the case it would have been only natural that some intercourse between them should take place; and I think that this is what happened round London.

Those who lay stress upon the small number of British words which we have taken over often fail to remind their readers that all the Londoners, when the Romans left, spoke Latin; and that it is in Latin rather than in Celtic words that the British influence must be sought. It cannot, I think, be said that the modern Englishman treats a late foe in a revengeful spirit, and it seems to me that there is every reason to believe that the Old

---

* It must be remembered that Ceawlin was deposed and driven into exile by a coalition between his own people and the Britons; and that, later on, Penda of Mercia allied himself with the British to attack Oswy of Northumbria.

English round London treated the citizens with the same moderation ; mixing with them enough to adopt certain of their place names, such as London, Thames, Dowgate and Ludgate ; allowing them, at the same time, to hand down many of their old customs.

When we look at a list of British words which have been taken into our language we must admit that it is small, but at the same time we must notice how many of them deal with every day details of the home, the workshop and the field ; and we cannot help feeling that the English must have learnt very much from the Britons. In order to do so they must have been brought into much closer contact with them than many writers have been willing to allow. Such a list, taken from Lathom's "English Language" gives us —*Basket, Balderdash, Boggle, Barrow, Button, Bother, Bran, Cart, Clout, Coat, Dainty, Darn, Fag* (as in fag end), *Fleam, Flaw, Funnel, Gyve, Grid, Gruel, Gown, Gusset, Hopper, Kiln, Mattock, Mop, Pelt, Rail, Rasher, Rug, Solder, Size* (glue), *Ted* (hay), *Tenter* (tenter hook), *Welt, Wicket, Wire.* The first of these—*basket*—alone suggests a line in which the British probably were most useful teachers ; since we know how skilful they were in wicker work, an art in which the Germanic tribes do not seem to have excelled, except perhaps in making the frames of their boats.

I am not trying to argue that there is a large quantity of British or Romano-British blood in the modern Englishman, I do not think that there is ; I am only trying to point out that there was every opportunity for the two peoples to mix, and that probably they did so round London, to a moderate degree. In the West Country, as the colour index points out, the mixture must have been greater, and since the Laws of Ine provide fines for damage done to Wealhs, some of which are quite heavy, it is clear that Britons formed a large part of his subjects.

It is very difficult to suggest even an approximate date for the occupation of London by the East Saxons. It seems reasonable to believe that so long as the Britons were fighting in Kent they used London as their base ; and, since they were defeated by Hengist and Aesc, and, seeking their base, " fled from them as fire " in A.D. 473, we may presume that London was not lost at that date. But when the fighting had shifted as far west as Mount Badon, the site of which cannot be identified, though we are told that it lay near the mouth of the Severn, it is very unlikely that London could still have been a military base. This battle is believed to have been fought in the first quarter of the sixth century, and evidently was the most serious check which the English received ; stopping any farther advance for more than half a century. During this time the scattered warriors became farmers and spent their time in developing what they had won, and in crystalising round various centres to form the different kingdoms, the names of which have come down to us.

Ceawlin, it already has been noticed, brought this quiescent period to an end in A.D. 577 by his vigorous advance into the valley of the Severn, and his capture of Bath, Cirencester and Gloucester ; but in 592 he was driven from the throne of Wessex and from his imperium or bretwaldaship, which made an opening for the younger Æthelbert of Kent to be called to that post. This king already had made himself overlord so far as the East of England was concerned ; and, in order to have done so, must have used London for establishing communications. Indeed, he is said to have had a palace in Aldermanbury.

This of course means that London by this time was English, and presumably had been so for some time. It is quite likely that, could we ask an East Saxon of those days as to when London first was occupied, he would be unable to say ; because the entry had been so cautious and imperceptible. At first it had been, perhaps, mere trading outside the walls, and then armed bands had passed through between Essex and Kent, greatly daring, because of the fiends and magic lurking among the temples and the other strange buildings. When it was found that nothing terrible ever happened, East Saxons may have stayed longer and longer in the city, until gradually they became townsmen, and London the recognised capital of Essex. But though it was Saebert's capital, Æthelbert of Kent was its over-lord ; and it was he who in A.D. 604 gave the see of London, which included Essex, Herts and

Surrey, to Mellitus, one of Augustine's companions.
Since Æthelbert had given the see of Rochester to
Justus, in order that he might rule spiritually over the
Kentish men, as already Augustine ruled over the
Men of Kent, it will be seen that London was the
third and not the first Bishopric founded in England by Gregory's missioners. It must be remembered however that there were many bishops of the
Welsh Church before these, and that Restitutus
has already been mentioned as Bishop of London
in A.D. 313, and Augulus somewhere about A.D. 340.

Mention of Surrey as part of the see of London
makes us want to know something of the early
history of that place. In A.D. 570 we found Æthelbert, as a boy, fighting with Ceawlin at Wimbledon,
and being driven back into Kent. After the
fight, therefore, the region must have belonged to
Ceawlin, and thus, to the West Saxons : but, as
Æthelbert grew older and more powerful, Ceawlin
seems to have seen in him a man equal in capacity
and energy to himself ; and, very wisely, these two
leaders of men realised that England was large
enough for both ; and, while Ceawlin was busy
reducing the West of the country, Æthelbert made
himself overlord of all the lands round London.

Ceawlin was a capable and successful warrior,
but Æthelbert, as I see him, was a cautious and
far seeing statesman ; a man who played a long
and winning game of chess with the East of England for his board. That he early made himself
master of Essex there seems no doubt ; perhaps it

would be more just to say that, by his wise and
temperate policy, he induced the East Saxons to
trust his judgment, and to take his advice in all
their tribal crises.   Æthelbert was no ruthless con-
queror ; and his boyish battle at Wimbledon is the
only record we have of his trying to increase his
power by military methods.   His later sway over
all England, as far as the Humber, seems to have
been established by wise diplomacy and to have
been a rule of love rather than of fear.

When Essex came under his influence he was
wise enough not to try to govern it himself, but to
place his nephew Saebert upon its throne, and to
help him to make London his capital.   Chadwick
thinks that the East Saxons crossed the river to
the West of London and annexed a piece of territory which undoubtedly had belonged to Wessex
hitherto.   Possibly this was done through the
diplomacy of Æthelbert, since Ceawlin was altogether occupied in the West, and may have been
glad to sell or exchange a region for which he now
cared little : but, in any case, it is difficult to see
why it should have been called Surrey, the Southern Kingdom, except by people who lived
North of it.   On this account Chadwick's suggestion seems a very likely one.   The early
Surrey must have been quite a narrow strip, for
the great forest of the Andredsweald lay just to the
South of it.

A great many Anglo-Saxon burial grounds have
been found in Surrey ; but the one nearest London

is that, already spoken of, at Mitcham. Its full description has not yet been published, but the general opinion seems to be that its cultural objects are of West Saxon type. In this there is nothing against Chadwick's theory, for the settlement at Mitcham probably was begun about A.D. 500 ; and there are signs that the burial ground was still in use in early Christian times, that is to say about A.D. 600, the time of which we are speaking. It seems almost certain that East Saxons, West Saxons and Angles became hopelessly mixed in many parts of England, and especially was this the case round London. We can only deplore that in the present state of our knowledge it is impossible to distinguish the different peoples by the physical characters of their skeletons and skulls.

I feel that little has been said here about the coming of Christianity to the Saxons, and of its welcome by Æthelbert and his queen Bertha ; but it is a Kentish story, and our knowledge of its effect upon London is small. Saebert of Essex built the first cathedral dedicated to St. Paul, and also founded the monastery at Westminster ; but here again, though the act was that of Saebert, the inspiration is likely to have come from his uncle and protector, Æthelbert. The conversion of the Londoners could not have been a very thorough one, for in A.D. 617, when Æthelbert and Saebert were dead, the two sons of the latter relapsed into heathenism, and drove Mellitus from his bishopric, which remained unfilled from that date until about 655, when Cedd was brought from the North by Sigebert the Good. It seems, therefore, that Saxon London was first nominally converted to Christianity by Rome ; but relapsed, and was reconverted by the Irish Church of Iona. This, later on, was forced to conform to Roman usages at the Synod of Whitby.

This Sigebert, though king of Essex, was subject to Oswy of Northumbria ; and London, therefore, acknowledged Northumbrian instead of Kentish overlordship at this time ; but Penda of Mercia defeated the pious Sigebert, who would fight only with a wand, lest he might injure anyone. Londoners thus found themselves owing allegiance to this brave but ferocious old heathen of Mercia. We do not gather that this change of overlordship made very much difference to London, a town which was on a different footing to that of any other in England ; since its position as the capital of Essex and the cathedral city of a wide bishopric was overshadowed by the fact that it was the centre of trade of the whole country. Bede, like Tacitus nearly seven centuries earlier, records that it was the abode of many merchants ; while its ships traded with all parts. The successive overlords, though they may have known little about trade, knew enough to appreciate that it meant tolls and fees and other incidental advantages ; and knew too that commerce and capital are shy birds, easily scared away by ignorant

interference. Very likely this is the main reason
why the customs and traditions of London changed
so little with its changing overlords. With regard
to the physical characteristics of its inhabitants at
this time, i.e., the middle of the seventh century,
we must believe that the greater number of the
townsmen were East Saxons, most of whom were
either freemen or freedmen ; since it seems that
when a serf was given or was able to buy his free-
dom, he tended to gravitate to the towns ; and
that, above these, were the foreign traders whose
stay in the city often was only temporary ; while
it is reasonable to suppose that below them there
was a class of serfs, many of whom must have been
of British origin.

As to when the Jews made their first appearance
in England it is difficult to decide. We know that
after the fall of Jerusalem in A.D. 70 they began to
wander among the Germanic tribes, and it would be
curious if, in the seventh century, none had reached
England. If they had done so it is unlikely that
they found much to attract them beyond London ;
unless it were Bristol, which about this time seems
to have had a large slave trade with Ireland. In
any case their numbers were not enough to have
brought them to the notice of Bede or his correspondents. On the whole, it does not seem that
the Jews made their presence felt seriously in
England until after the Norman conquest.

That Bede knew what was going on in London,
although he had never been there, is shown by his

indignation at the bargain which Wulfhere, Penda's son, made with Wini of Winchester ; by
which the bishopric of London was sold for money,
a shocking case of simony, though seemingly it
had no evil consequences for Wini.

Very little is heard of London during the later
years of the seventh century ; though it must
surely have been developing and organising its
wonderful position as a trading centre. That it
became subject to Ine, the lawgiving king of
Wessex, seems probable ; because he talks, in
A.D. 693, of Earconswald, one of London's great
bishops, as "my bishop." Indeed, whenever the
king of one state established an imperium over a
number of the others, London seems to have fallen
to his share ; though, as we have seen, he was
always too wise to do more than collect tribute
from it.

The eighth century, like the latter part of the
seventh, is singularly bare of records about
London.   Bede died in A.D. 735, and we miss
his anecdotes and cleverly drawn word pictures
of events.   We know that the power of Wessex
waned ; and that Mercia, under Ethelbald, once
more became the chief kingdom of the South
of England ; that in 752 Cuthred, at the battle of
Burford in Oxfordshire, regained the supremacy of
Wessex, and that in 771 Offa of Mercia had, as
his vassals, the kings of Wessex and Kent.   About
Essex and London nothing is heard, though we
may safely assume that the city became the

spoil of the winner, and was passed backward and forward like a shuttlecock. Offa was regarded by Charlemagne as the king of England rather than of Mercia, and seems to have been in London a good deal. Indeed some think that it was he, and not Sæbert, who founded the abbey of Thorney which, later on, was to be known as Westminster.

In 787 two papal legates were present at the council of Cealchythe, a place which Oman, following Lingard, identifies with Chelsea. At first sight this seems unlikely, since Cealchythe means a chalk landing place; while Chelsea usually is derived from *ceosel eg*, the Saxon for pebble island. I see, however, that in Domesday Book Chelsea is called *Chelched*, which looks much more like a corruption of Cealchythe than of ceosel *eg* (chesel eye). And so it seems Lingard was right, though what Chelsea had to do with chalk I do not know. At this council, among other things, the see of Canterbury was divided, and a third primacy established at Lichfield. The degradation of Canterbury, however, seems to have been an act of revenge on Offa's part against Archbishop Jaenbert, and only lasted for sixteen years. The Witenagemot of A.D. 820 is the first recorded as having been held in London. Its object was to settle a rather unimportant quarrel between Coenwulf, king of Mercia, and Wulfred, archbishop of Canterbury, but its happening at all shows that London was still under Mercian influence.

CHAPTER VIII

LONDON AND THE DANES

IN A.D. 829, Egbert of Wessex became Bretwalda and is often looked upon as the first king of all England; though it is doubtful whether Offa really is not more worthy of the title. In Egbert's days the long and wearisome tale of civil war comes to an end, for Englishmen had now, for the first time, to face a foreign invader in the Dane; a foe so terrible that fighting among themselves would have been madness. In this we see that the psychology of the Saxons was different from that of the Celts; for when the former were invading Britain, the Britons, Gildas says, were fighting one with the other; but when the Danes attacked England, the English sank their internal quarrels and united against the common foe.

The Danes at first, it is thought, came from Scandinavia, and many of them, wandering South, had occupied the peninsula of Jutland, as well as the country south of it; and it may be that the forcible conversion of the continental Saxons to Christianity by Charlemagne—for it must be remembered that to a Frank any northern neighbour of

another tribe was a Saxon—irritated and unsettled
all the people who dwelt north of him so much
that they took to piracy ; at first out of revenge,
and then from their love of the excitement, danger,
and rich spoils of the life.

Their invasion of England was wonderfully like
that of their kinsmen the Saxons four centuries
earlier. Indeed they seem to have been in just
the same stage of culture as that in which the
Saxons were when first they landed on these
shores. To begin with there were merely pira-
tical raids such as that at Lindisfarne in 793 ;
and then organized landings from larger and larger
fleets ; as success made them bolder, and practice
gave them experience. England was not their
only objective, for the Franks and Frisians
suffered even more at their hands, as indeed they
should have done if Charlemagne's action started
the trouble. Ireland, too, with its rich monasteries, and the disjointed opposition of many petty
kings, was a favourite prey for many years.

We see, I think, in these raids the same unforeseen, lightning like movements which have always
characterized the Nordic peoples ; movements
undertaken with little forethought or preparation,
and yet often succeeding because of their unex-
pectedness and audacity. Sometimes, of course,
they failed, but, wasp like, would be tried again
by the same fighters or their successors. The
simile of the wasp is not altogether a fair one—
similes seldom are—for the Danes learned by

experience, which the wasp seldom does. They learned the importance of forming a fortified base camp, usually upon an island, where their ships might lie, and to which they could retire when the opposition became too strong for them. They learned too the importance of mobility on land as well as at sea ; and after a time one of their first acts upon landing was to sieze all the neighbouring horses, and thus change themselves from seamen into light infantry whose movements it was very difficult to foresee or to provide against.

The English fyrd or militia, under the alderman of the district attacked, was always ready and willing to face them ; but the Danes had the advantage of constant war service, while the English were militia who, perhaps, might not have been called out for many years and certainly had neither the discipline nor the fighting experience of the invaders. Nothing, I think, speaks so highly for the character and courage of the Saxons as the way in which, without proper training or defensive armour, they could always be relied upon to attack and follow up the highly trained, ring-mailed, Viking bands whenever they appeared. Of course the most serious mistake the English ever made was that of losing command of the sea. Alfred realized this ; but the command, once gone, was not so easily regained ; and during their four hundred years of land fighting and farming, Englishmen seem to have lost for a time the sea sense which once was theirs.

The Danes, Swedes and Norwegians evidently were closely alike physically, and had the same long narrow heads, long faces and aquiline features which characterized the Anglo-Saxons.

We are indebted to Gustav Retzius for a magnificent piece of work, known as "Crania Suesica," in which life size photographs are shown of the skulls of Swedes belonging to the stone, bronze and iron ages. The latter, of course, were of the Viking period, and many of these iron age skulls, no doubt, belonged to Swedish vikings, and resembled pretty closely those of the Norwegians and Danes. An average contour of them shows all the characters of the Nordic skull ; but the pity is that these photographs were taken before the importance of contour tracings was understood ; and it will be found that, beautiful as they are as works of art, they are not altogether reliable for measurements owing to the perspective effects of photography.

The first experience of the Danes which London had was in A.D. 851, while Æthelwulf, the father of Alfred, was king of England. The City at this time still was associated with Mercia ; and the Mercian sub-king, Beorhtwulf, stoutly defended it ; but was put to flight and his metropolis plundered. After this the Danes went south into Surrey ; but Æthelwulf, with the army of Wessex, met them at Aclea and inflicted upon them the most crushing defeat they had hitherto known in England. Oman thinks that this Aclea was Oakley near

Basingstoke ; though the traditional view is that it is Ockley near Horsham. The question is forcibly, though a little bitterly, argued by Hillaire Belloc in his book on " Stone Street," and perhaps, had Oman possessed the local knowledge of Belloc, he would have been content with Ockley in *Surrey*, which is *South* of London and close to the junction of the *Stane Street*, down which the Danes had passed, and the *Pilgrims' Way*, along which Æthelwulf was hurrying from Wessex. The position of Aclea affects London only indirectly ; but the victory cleared the country of invaders for a year or two, and thus was of great importance. We now pass over twenty years, during which the Danes were fighting hard with Æthelwulf and his sons. The heathens had made the North and East of England their own, but seem to have realized that they might never subdue the whole country so long as men like Æthelbert, Æthelred and Alfred were at large : hence they left Mercia and London, its capital, alone for a time, and concentrated all their efforts upon Wessex.

During this heroic struggle the men of London, Mercia and Kent seem to have lost their old warlike spirit ; though possibly their inertia was due to lack of leaders, without which the best fighting material is useless. They did not understand, though the Danes seem to have seen it plainly enough, that if Wessex fell England would become Danish.

It was at the close of this period, in A.D. 872, that

Alfred was obliged to buy off the Danes.   To have carried on the struggle would have meant hopeless disaster for war worn Wessex ;   while a truce, though it lasted only a year or two, might give a chance of recovery.   As it happened the result showed his wisdom

During the furious fighting in the West Country between Alfred and Guthrum, which followed the former's leaving Athelney, nothing is heard of London ; but in A.D. 879, after the Danish chief had been defeated and baptised, a new force of Danes sailed up the Thames and fortified itself at Fulham, though it stayed there only a short time.

Apparently London remained in the hands of the Danes after the peace of Chippenham or Wedmore ;   and went to Guthrum with East Mercia, Essex and East Anglia, until in 886 it was recovered by Alfred in a very ruinous state, and handed over to Æthelred, the alderman of West Mercia who had lately married Æthelflaed, Alfred's eldest daughter.

This is a time of great moment to the anthropologist interested in London though the details are few and meagre.   Seemingly Alfred had a hard fight to wrest the city from the Danes ; but after driving them out, he rebuilt the walls and repeopled the town with military settlers.   These of course, may have been refugees from the Danelagh ;   though it seems more likely that, for the greater part, they were Mercians lately serving under Æthelred, the alderman of Mercia to whom its rulership was given. It is said by some authorities that the modern English which we speak and write is Mercian in its kinship, and if this be so, it is quite possible that the fact is due to the resettlement of the City by Alfred : for modern literary English, in the main, evolved itself in London.

When the Danes held London, a great many of the original inhabitants must either have been driven out, or have left of their own accord ; otherwise it is difficult to see why Alfred should have found it necessary to people it once more ; and these new burghware must have been the main forefathers of the mediæval and modern Londoners down to the eighteenth century.

Three large collections of seventeenth and eighteenth century London skeletons have been examined carefully of late years ; from Whitechapel,* Moorfields† and Clare market. The measurements and characters of these are very much alike, and also like those of the Saxons. It is true that it has been thought that there is a likeness to the Long Barrow Folk in the first two series ; though this claim has recently been withdrawn. In any case there is no evidence to account for Long Barrow People persisting in London in larger numbers than elsewhere in the South East of England.

In A.D. 895, Alfred, with the Londoners, captured the whole fleet of the Danes who had foolishly taken it a long way up the Lea. It was, of course,

* Biometrika, vol. 3, p. 191.   † Ibid, vol. 5, p. 86.

quite easy to block the river below the point at which the enemy lay, and thus to force them to abandon all their ships and escape overland.

The next point of importance in London's history is that on the death of Æthelred, the alderman of Mercia, in 910, Edward the Elder, who was Alfred's son and successor, took it back under his own rule. He does not seem to have lived much in it ; or, indeed, anywhere else for long ; since the greater part of his reign was spent in winning back the Midlands and Eastern Counties from the Danes. With the exception of Alfred, none of the kings of the house of Egbert seems to have taken any great interest in London until the time of Æthelred the Redeless. They were crowned at Kingston, it is true, but it does not seem that London took any part in the ceremony.

Perhaps it is not surprising that notices of London should be so poor in the Anglo-Saxon Chronicle, since this was a West Saxon production associated with Winchester ; while London was at this time a Mercian town ; or, at all events, a town with Mercian associations. It is asking too much of human nature to expect the organ of one capital city to advertise the successful development of a rival.

Trevelyan (*History of England*) notices what a much better trader the Dane made than the Saxon. It is common knowledge that real trading, as opposed to mere hawking or peddling, needs, and soon creates, a town in which it may thrive.

The Saxons, we know, were farmers and hunters rather than traders, and had a marked dislike to town life, which probably was their greatest point of contrast with the Danes. The influence of this psychological difference may be traced in London's history ; for, under the Romans, it arose and became an important city ; but, in Saxon times, its importance waned and it was not until after Alfred's day, when Danish influence was felt, that once more it gradually became the great mart of the kingdom ; and able, at and after the Norman Conquest, to take the lead in settling the policy of England.

When Edgar was upon the throne England was happy and prosperous, and London we may believe was growing in wealth and influence. The real control of the country seems to have been in the hands of Dunstan, whose character was as complex and interesting as any in history. One of his many sides was that of a capable, unscrupulous politician and trickster, and the fact that he took the bishopric of London in 959, on his way to the primacy, shows that he regarded that see as one of the most important in the kingdom ; and a step up from the bishopric of Worcester, the original Mercian capital, where King Edgar lived.

When Æthelred the Redeless came to the throne, sore trouble fell upon England ; for he had no capacity or character of his own, and his lack of judgment always made him listen to worthless counsellors. Indeed the whole story of Saxon

England impresses upon us the fact that without a king of character and judgment the country could do nothing. It may be argued that the history of Edgar the Peacemaker, which has just been quoted, is directly opposed to this conclusion ; but it must be remembered that, though the brain which ruled England in his time seems to have been that of Dunstan, it would have been powerless had Edgar not marked this crafty cleric as the owner of the best brain in the country ; and had he not supported him loyally in his far sighted statesmanship. I have just called this brilliant scholar a sordid and unscrupulous trickster, and so he was ; but he had many other sides, some of which in modern days would have landed him in a lunatic asylum, others in a gaol ; but one of his many facets showed prudent statesmanship of a high order ; and it was this side of him which Edgar had the judgment to discern and use.

In A.D. 894, Olaf Trygvesson, a Norwegian, and Sweyn of Denmark, whose name suggests his Swedish origin, sailed up the Thames and attacked London ; but the burgh-ware, whom Alfred had settled there, made such a splendid resistance that the enemy was forced to withdraw ; though Æthelred characteristically did nothing to help the City.

In A.D. 1009, another attack was made on London ; but the Londoners again were true to themselves and their city, and beat off their assailants.

Three years later Norwegians, in alliance with

Danes, brought Archbishop Ælpheah or Alphege
to Greenwich from Canterbury, as a hostage ;
while Æthelred was in London collecting danegelt
with which to buy them off. It was here that
some drunken Norsemen murdered the poor old
man with ox bones and horns, because he would
not pay them an extra ransom ; though it is only
fair to add that Thorkil, their leader, knew nothing
about it, and at once handed over the archbishop's
body to the Londoners for burial in St. Paul's.

Soon after this the people not only of the Danelagh but of places like Winchester and Oxford were
so disgusted with their cowardly and incompetent
king that they welcomed Sweyn. London, however
again beat him off, and it was not until all the rest
of England had taken him for their king that the
Londoners had to follow suit, and sent in their
submission in A.D. 1014.

Æthelred retired to Normandy, where he had
already sent his wife Emma and their two sons,
Alfred and Edward, placing them in the care of
his brother-in-law, Richard, the Norman Duke.

As it happened Sweyn was to live only eleven
days after his accession ; and Æthelred returned
to dispute the kingdom with Knut, the son of the
dead king. Once more London opened its gates to
him, and acted as his centre until he died there in
A.D. 1016. It is interesting to notice how Æthelred turned to London as his troubles increased.
He must have realized that it was not only the
strongest town but that its inhabitants were the

best fighting force in the kingdom.   Moreover, the
wretched creature knew that London was Saxon
all through, and that, in spite of his shameful conduct, the fact that he was an English king would
never be forgotten there.

After the death of this worst of the old English
kings, his son Edmund Ironside, who was a brave
man fighting against heavy odds, carried on the
struggle for the throne with Knut ; and London is
now in the centre of the picture.   Æthelred had
hardly been buried, when Knut besieged the city,
and cut the memorable canal round Southwark, in order to get his ships on to the upper
river without runnning the gauntlet of the bridge
and its garrison.   He could make no impression, however, on the Londoners ; and, after Edmund had defeated him at the battle of Brentford,
he retired to Greenwich or, more probably, Blackheath, where remnants of a camp, believed to
be Danish, have been found.   It is thought by
some that the second half of the name Greenwich
is derived from the Norse *vik*, a creek ; and of
course the creek at Greenwich is there to-day ;
though there is no such thing, now at all events,
either at Woolwich or Dulwich.   Deptford, too,
it has been suggested is the deep *fiord* ; while
Shooter's Hill, which must have been a prominent
landmark to the Danes sailing up the river, is
thought to be a variant of the two Danish words
shaw and *tor*, the wooded hill.   The derivation of
place names, however, needs too much research

and training to allow us lightly to welcome a suggestion because it fits in with our views ; but I think, however, that it should be understood that for a great many years the Danes held the district south-east of London, especially in the neighbour-hood of Greenwich ; and are more likely to have camped on the gravel plateau of Blackheath than in the marshes of Greenwich itself. It can easily be imagined what a serious thing for London a force of Danes astride of Watling Street must have been.

The behaviour of the mixed hordes of Danish and Norse invaders in England gives us a further insight into the primitive Nordic mentality. It sometimes is said that the ideals of these people were wonderfully like those of boys at our English public schools to-day ; and the comparison seems in many ways a happy one. The sins which the Norseman never could forgive were cowardice and treachery, by which he understood obtaining any advantage by means of deceit. But this standard of truthfulness and loyalty was only expected among comrades and did not apply to dea ings with the enemy, for we find the Danes again and again breaking their most solemn engagements in a way which would have ruined the reputation of any public school eleven or fifteen.

It may seem unjustifiable to compare bloodshed and slaughter with boyish games ; but in the two undeveloped groups about which we are speaking they really are quite comparable, forming, as they did or do, the main object of life for the time being—the one in striving for which character is built up and has a fair chance of showing itself in its true colours. In one particular, however, there is a marked difference between the two ; for boastfulness or bragging, either before or after the contest is " bad form " to the public schoolboy of to-day ; while the Norseman recognised the " bragging cup " as an institution and freely indulged in it.

We return from this digression to Edmund and Knut, the effect of whose rivalry was that the country was divided between them, much as it had been in the days of Alfred and Guthrum ; and, when Edmund died, Knut succeeded to the whole kingdom.

On the whole Knut made a very creditable English King, and seems thoroughly to have understood his new subjects. It is true that he raised a huge tribute from the country, but he used it to pay off the great Danish army which was quartered on England. Ten thousand five hundred pounds of silver were exacted from London alone ; which shows what a rich city it was, even in those days. Only a few of his countrymen were given large estates, among whom was Osgod Clapa whose share included the whole of South Lambeth, and whose hall presumably was at Clapham, which hands down his name. It is possible, too, that at this time of the disbandment of the great army, some of Knut's countrymen formed a settlement outside the City, beside the

Mill stream and its spring, the Holy well, in the Strand. Here they built a Church which they dedicated to St. Clement ; for, like their king, they had lately become Christians. In the foundations of the present St. Clement Danes pre-Norman work may still be seen ; while those of us who are old enough remember Holliwell Street which was cleared away when the Strand improvements began, and which handed down the name of the Holy Well.

How much Danish blood actually found its way into the population of London is difficult to determine. Probably this separate colony outside the walls, which was only large enough to need one Church, contained all the Danes in the neighbourhood of the city ; though it is fairly certain that they were absorbed into the general population very quickly. Certainly the Danish element was not nearly so great as in the northern, midland and eastern counties, where it still shows itself in the low colour index, as well as in place names.

It is quite possible that more Norwegian than Danish blood was introduced into London about this time, for Thorkil had made peace with Ethelred ; and he, with his Norse followers, were in London, helping in its defence against the Danes under Sweyn. When it is remembered that there are three churches dedicated to St. Olaf (Haraldson) in different parts of London, it looks as though the Norse congregations were not only more numerous but more closely blended with the other Londoners than were the Danes, who dwelt without the city walls.

Probably the skulls and bones of the Saxons and Danes were so much alike that our present knowledge would not enable us to distinguish them; though I am glad to think that I still have contour

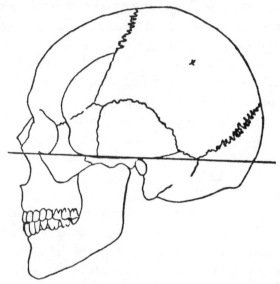

FIG. 23. A composite tracing of the profiles of 30 male, eighteenth century, skulls from the region of Clare market. This average, modern Londoner's skull form may be compared with Figs. 6, 11 and 16.

drawings, to scale, of a large number of 18th century skulls, taken from the old site of King's College Hospital where once had been a graveyard of St. Clement Danes. When we have a really representative series of Saxon skull contours, which I hope will be very soon, as well as some of Danish vikings (we have Swedish vikings already), a careful study and comparison will be possible ; but it is the spade work of collecting reliable material which takes the time.

And now the task of reviewing the earlier inhabitants of London comes to a close. My allotted space is filled, and though I would gladly discuss the influence of Duke William and his Norman knights, and could do so easily in a few pages, the consideration of the motley crowd which formed more than half his following would need more space than is given me.

We leave London, as Harold knew it, inhabited by people of whom probably seven eighths were of Nordic blood, derived firstly from the Cymric Brythons and Belgae ; secondly, from the Gaulish legions of Rome ; thirdly, from the Teutonic Anglo-Saxons, chiefly East Saxons and Mercians ; and fourthly from the Danes ; among whom were large numbers of Norwegians and Swedes. The Mercians, it must be remembered, were a mixture of West Saxons and Angles. Whether the Men of Kent, who we have seen were called Jutes, but probably were largely Franks, found their way into London to any appreciable extent is doubtful; though the Kentish Men, in whom Frisian blood seems to have been plentiful, doubtless settled in Southwark.*

The Mediterranean Race can have formed only a

* Bede tells a story of a Saxon youth, named Imma, who, being taken captive by a Mercian thegn, was sold by him to a Freson as a slave.

small percentage of London's inhabitants in those days; since the city was twice largely repeopled by Nordics, once by East Saxons, and again in Alfred's time. Still, a little of the Long Barrow and earlier Neolithic strain no doubt survived, and perhaps even a very little of the blood of the Italian and Greek merchants who followed the Roman legions; though these legions we have seen were seldom of Italian blood, and we should think twice before we talk lightly of our " Roman ancestors."

The small proportion of the Alpine Race present in London before the Conquest came partly from the Beaker Folk and " Prospectors," and partly from the small strain which the Saxons brought over with them from North Germany.

The modern Londoner no doubt has received a great deal of both Alpine and Mediterranean blood since the Norman Conquest ; and the Alpine type, especially, seems to be increasing at the present time. The research, however, which I have been able to make among the hospital patients and medical students of London makes me sure that the modern Londoner is still more than three-quarters Nordic in his characteristics, though I am conscious that a new type of head form is gradually being evolved ; a type for which neither Mendelism nor reversion will account.

INDEX

233